Waterstone's Guide to History Books

Edited by Nick Rennison

Contents

Thousands of history books are published each year. The backlists of publishers contain many thousands more. For the reader with an interest in the past that is not academic or specialist the range of books available can seem intimidating. What is the most accessible one-volume history of the French Revolution? Where should one look for information about Roman Britain? What is the most comprehensive and up-to-date biography of Gladstone? This guide is designed to answer these questions and many more that the general reader might ask when confronted by the serried ranks of titles on the history shelves. It is a selection of nearly 750 history books, on subjects ranging from Tutankhamun to the British Labour party, from the Celtic empire to Stalin's purges in the thirties. Each title selected is accompanied by a brief, explanatory review written by a Waterstone's bookseller. The guide also includes a series of brief essays focusing on a particular subject of interest - the Wars of the Roses, the Vikings, the history of Scotland - which list more titles on that subject than it was possible to review in the main text. In addition there are essays by major contemporary historians, including Felipe Fernandez-Armesto, Roy Porter and Linda Colley, on themes which interest them particularly and there are money-off offers on books published by three major publishers of history titles. Waterstone's has always been committed to stocking a substantial range of history books in all its branches. We hope that this guide will direct the general reader through that range to the title for which he or she is searching.

Historiography

Barraclough, Geoffrey
An Introduction to Contemporary History
Penguin pbk £7.99
0140135138

Barraclough was a distinguished historian of Germany and the editor of the original edition of the *Times Atlas of World History*. This is his survey of the main themes of contemporary history - the changes wrought in our views of the nature of politics in the light of the changes in the fundamental structures of world politics, the impact of science and the spread of technology and the challenge of modern ideologies, particularly Marxism.

Bloch, Marc
The Historian's Craft
Manchester UP pbk £11.95
071903292X

Marc Bloch (1886 -1944) was the founder, together with Lucien Febvre, of *Annales* which first appeared in 1929 and proved to be the most influential historical journal published this century, radically affecting the way historians, in France and throughout the world, approached the task of writing social, economic and cultural history. This book, published posthumously, offers Bloch's thoughts on the uses and methods of history and his ideas on historical analysis and the nature of historical causation. It is a valuable introduction to the broad philosophy of what has come to be known as the Annales school of historians.

Carr, E.H.
What Is History?
Penguin pbk £6.99
0140135847

First published more than 30 years ago these stimulating reflections on the nature of history by a distinguished historian aroused much discussion with their insistence on the historian's inability to view the past with detached objectivity. Carr's argument that all historians are necessarily conditioned and their work largely determined by the society and class in which they write provided a forcible rejection of old liberal beliefs about the possibility of historical objectivity.

Collingwood, R.G.
The Idea of History
Oxford UP pbk £9.99
0192853066

Collingwood (1889-1943) was a professor of philosophy at Oxford who was also a significant figure in the study of the history and archaeology of Roman Britain. His book *Roman Britain and the English Settlements*, published in 1936, remains important in the field, despite the huge growth of knowledge brought about by excavations and scholarly work since the war. *The Idea of History*, published posthumously, constitutes his own reflections on the nature of history and the differing concepts of it through the ages.

Elton, G.R.
The Practice of History
Fontana pbk £7.99
0006861334

Published at least in part as a response to Carr's *What is History*, Elton's book is a crucial text in the debate between those who see history as moulded and shaped by the preconceptions of historians themselves and those, like Elton, prepared to defend the notion of an objective truth to be approached by historians through impartial assessment of the evidence. Elton's witty and forthright pronouncements on history and his fellow historians enliven a book that has become a classic of modern historiography.

Hobsbawm, Eric & Ranger, Terence
The Invention of Tradition
Cambridge UP pbk £7.95
0521437733

It is often assumed that most of the traditions in which Britain is so rich are ancient in their origins and dignified by the passage of centuries. In truth, as this varied collection of essays shows, many of the best-known traditions were invented comparatively recently. The essays deal with a number of subjects - from the creation of Welsh and Scottish 'national' culture to the elaboration of rituals attached to the royal family - and throw fresh light on ongoing debates about the nature of our historical inheritance and the present's relationship with the past.

Lowenthal, David
The Past Is a Foreign Country
Cambridge UP pbk £18.95
0521294800

Lowenthal is a writer and academic who has a particular interest in the ways the past and the present interact and in the ways people interpret and refashion the past. In this book he draws on literary and documentary evidence from the arts, the humanities and the social sciences to throw light on how man has come to terms with the past since the Renaissance.

Marwick, Arthur
The Nature of History
Macmillan pbk £12.99
0333432355

The Nature of History provides the student and the interested reader with a comprehensive introduction to the arguments and issues in historiography. His summaries of the views of all the major participants in the debate, a debate that is itself subject to historical change and development, are fair and concise and the excellent glossary, collection of quotations and bibliography which conclude the book point the way towards further study.

Tosh, John
The Pursuit of History
Longman pbk £13.99
0582026342

Any student wanting a general introduction to history as an intellectual discipline is likely to find John Tosh's book an invaluable and accessible read. He looks at the most basic questions one can ask about the writing of history. Why should we study history? How do we construct our knowledge of the past and how objective, if at all, can it be? He also examines the different kinds of history being written today and the new perspectives provided by an emphasis on subjects for study, such as gender, which have been neglected until recently.

British History – General

Briggs, Asa
A Social History of England
Penguin pbk £8.99
0140136061

'Of the many kinds of history', writes Asa Briggs, 'social history was in the past often thought of as more trivial than constitutional, political or military history. They dealt with great events: it dealt with everyday things.....In recent years, however, all this has changed. Social history has now become a favourite kind of history, and as its range and methods have expanded, it has attracted more and more serious study.' This vigorous narrative social history of England from the Upper Paleolithic to the present day provides a synthesis of some of that scholarship and provides it in a form that is readily accessible to the general reader.

Fryer, Peter
Staying Power: Black People in Britain
Pluto Press pbk £13.99
0861047745

It is often assumed that black Britons did not exist before this century. In fact the black population of London in the eighteenth century was somewhere between ten and fifteen thou-

sand and black faces would have been a commonplace sight. There were black soldiers and black sailors, black prostitutes and black authors. Fryer's book is a wide-ranging history of black people and their experiences in Britain through several centuries.

Haigh, Christopher
Cambridge Historical Encyclopedia of Great Britain and Ireland
Cambridge UP pbk £17.95
0521395526

Successfully combining the elements of a reference work with a continuous history of Britain, this massive collaboration between sixty scholars offers both short, descriptive entries and longer, interpretive essays. The key dates and events not only in English history but also Irish history, Scottish history and Welsh history are covered and the book concludes with a biographical who's who of the great, the good and the infamous. Throughout it is well illustrated with maps, charts and photographs.

Halliday, F. E.
A Concise History of England
Thames & Hudson pbk £7.95
0500271828

First published in the sixties, this one-volume introduction to English history has been revised several times and continues to offer an engaging survey, from Stonehenge to the present-day, aimed at those who, in Halliday's words, 'welcome a History of England short enough to be grasped - and seen - as a whole.' The book is highly readable and carries illustration on nearly every page.

Hibbert, Christopher
The English: A Social History
HarperCollins pbk £10.99
0586084711

Hibbert's fascinating history of the daily life of English people through nine centuries draws effectively on letters, memoirs, diaries, official reports and literature to provide clear insights into English society at work and play through the generations. Written with Hibbert's customary fluency and with his eye for the telling example and anecdote, this is a book that was justifiably

Hoskins, W. G.

The Making of the English Landscape

Penguin pbk £9.99

0140154108

Hoskins' book has been in print since the fifties and has long been accepted as the standard work on its subject. He examines the landscape as we know it today and shows, through a detailed and easily comprehensible text and enlightening illustrative material, how what we see has been shaped by centuries of historical development and by the long and varied action of man - as farmer, builder and developer - on the natural world. Nature, in this country at least, is more a product of man and less a given than most of us suspect.

Johnson, Paul

The Offshore Islanders

Phoenix pbk £9.99

1857993810

Paul Johnson is well known as a journalist of forceful, often controversial views. He is, perhaps, less well known as an historian. However, as he writes in the prologue to his interpretation of two thousand years of English history, 'it is wrong to draw too sharp a distinction between the journalist and the historian. They are both in the same business: to communicate an understanding of events to the reader.' Certainly Johnson has succeeded in producing a work which is polemical, often oblivious to fashionable notions of political correctness, but which is also an exceptionally readable narrative of English history from the time of the Romans to the years of Thatcherism.

described by John Mortimer on its first publication as 'an admirable evocation of the past and a lasting analysis of the English character.'

Hibbert, Christopher

The Story of England

Phaidon pbk £9.99

0714826529

Christopher Hibbert is renowned as a gifted and versatile popular historian. In this book he rises to the challenge of encompassing the broad outline of England's political, economic and cultural history from Neolithic times to the 1990s in a narrative of 200 pages. The result is a generously illustrated introduction to the history of England for the general reader and for tourists and travellers who wish to set the places they visit in their historical context. The book also includes maps, genealogies of English monarchs, a list of Prime Ministers and a brief bibliography to lead the interested reader further.

Morgan, Kenneth (ed)

Oxford Illustrated History of Britain

Oxford UP pbk £13.95

0192851748

This is a comprehensive and accessible introduction to the history of Britain, written by a number of different scholars, each a distinguished interpreter of the period on which he writes. The quality and extent of the illustration gives added value to the book.

Reproduced from *The Oxford Illustrated History of Tudor and Stuart Britain (Oxford)*.

Re-telling the Nation's Story

David Cannadine

The general editor of the new Penguin History of Britain reflects on changing methods of writing the nation's history

Whether there is now, or has ever been, such a thing as 'the' national past is endlessly (and rightly) debated. There have always been different versions of the nation and its history, depending on the location, class, religion, gender, politics and ethnicity of the beholder and the historian. Britain's past looks different when viewed from Brixton or Belgravia, Birmingham or Belfast. There is also a more general way in which a people's sense of their national past can be influenced by changes in their domestic well-being and global standing. Top nations view their histories differently from rising or falling or bottom nations.

These popular perceptions of the national past are not only varied and changing. They also co-exist with the accounts which historians - sometimes amateurs, but more usually professionals and academics - provide. Thus regarded, historians are the keepers of our collective national memory - or collective national memories. For they, too, approach the past from many different personal and professional perspectives. And these perspectives are themselves subject to change. New methodologies, new approaches, new controversies, new information about the past: all this can change what we read and what we are told about the nation and its history.

In our own case, this argument may be unfolded across many centuries. After all, the Venerable Bede compiled his *History of the English Church and Nation* in A.D. 731, and since then national history has continually been made and remade, national history has regularly been written and re-written, and national identity has varied, changed and evolved in consequence. The links between these developments are themselves a fit subject of historical enquiry. Even if we confine ourselves to the last one hundred and fifty years or so, we can get some sense of how they connect, and see how the ways we have looked at our nation and its past have changed since the time of Queen Victoria.

The most fashionable national histories written during the Queen's reign were those multi-volumed, single-authored works of which Macaulay's *History of England*, published in four volumes between 1855 and 1861, was the pre-eminent example. Towards the end of her reign, these leisurely surveys were replaced by single volume histories, most notably J.R.Green's *Short History of the English People*, which held the field until G.M. Trevelyan's *History of England* was published in 1926. By this time, the third version of our nation's history was also well-established : those multi-volume, multi-authored works, written by a team of academic professionals, as published by Methuen, Longmans and Oxford University Press.

These Victorian and post-Victorian versions of our national past varied greatly in content and quality. But they were all written by authors who took history seriously and who sought to reach a wide public audience; they stressed the centuries-long dimensions of our national story; they were mainly, though not exclusively, concerned with political history; and they applauded English exceptionalism, took for granted that England was the greatest nation in the world, and devoted relatively little space to the histories of Ireland, Scotland and Wales. Since the Second World War, similar histories have continued to appear. But in recent decades, changes in the nation state, in Britain's position in the world, and in history writing itself, have increasingly called into question this approach to the past.

The erosion of national sovereignty has been one of the most marked features of the post-modern world, and decisions affecting Britain are increasingly taken in Brussels, Tokyo, New York or Hong Kong. Instead of being seen as something sacrosanct and immutable, the nineteenth and twentieth-century nation state is now regarded as merely one way of organising large numbers of people, which rests on manufactured myths and invented traditions. And Britain itself is no longer a global great power, separate from 'Europe', but a multi-racial society, in which the different identities of the Irish, Scots and Welsh are regularly re-affirmed, and where many institutions which have for so long seemed the very emblem of national identity, from the monarchy and parliament downwards, no longer command the automatic respect they once did.

There have also been significant developments in historical research and writing since 1945. Traditional political and constitutional history have been carried on; but they have been challenged and joined by new, burgeoning sub-disciplines, which have greatly increased our understanding of the past, but which are less concerned with national boundaries and the nation-state : economic history, social history, urban history, and the histories of technology, population, women and ideas. And at the same time, English history has been faced with a specific and no less powerful challenge: the emergence of Irish, Welsh and Scottish history as separate, self-conscious academic subjects.

These recent developments make the traditional histories conceived during the heyday of the English nation state and the British Empire look old-fashioned and outmoded. But this does not mean that we should abandon the idea that national histories can and should be written. Rumours of the death of the nation state may yet turn out to be exaggerated, and the forces holding the United Kingdom together may yet prove stronger than those pulling it apart. And whatever the future holds for our nation, some knowledge of its past will still be essential for anyone who wants to understand how we got to be where we are and the way we are.

The challenge of writing our national history has thus not become less pressing: instead it has become more difficult. Writing the history of Britain in the late twentieth century is not the same as writing the history of England in the late nineteenth century. Striking the balance between the public history of politics, government and international relations, and the very different but no less important history of ordinary peoples' lives, is never easy. And taking into account the massive outpouring of scholarly work on almost every conceivable aspect of the past, while writing vigorous and accessible prose, is difficult in ways that only those who have tried their hands at it can know. It is a daunting but exhilarating task.

Macaulay, Thomas Babington
History of England
Penguin pbk £8.99
0140431330
Macaulay (1800 - 1859) was one of the leading intellectual figures of Victorian England and renowned in his lifetime as a poet, essayist, politician and historian. Although some of the lines of his *Lays of Ancient Rome* remain familiar, his fame today rests largely on the *History of England*, a classic of English historical writing. Macaulay intended originally to demonstrate his belief in the rightness and adaptability of the English Constitution in a huge narrative of events from 1688 to the eve of the Great Reform Bill but he lowered his aim to 1714 and had reached only 1697 when he died. Macaulay was a man of boundless self-confidence - Melbourne famously remarked, 'I wish I was as cocksure of anything as Tom Macaulay is of everything.' - and his exposition of the 'Whig' view of history can appear, to contemporary readers, a callow and complacent assertion of the superiority of the English form of government over all foreign forms of government, and the superiority of the class to which he belonged over all other classes. However there is no mistaking his superb skills as a narrative historian and his eye for dramatic set-pieces and his History, which has never been out of print since first publication, remains vividly readable.

Kearney, Hugh
The British Isles
Cambridge UP pbk £7.95
052148488X
This is an introduction to the history of the British Isles from pre-Roman times to the twentieth century which is distinguished by its adoption of what Kearney calls a 'Britannic' approach. He believes that the histories of what are often regarded as four nations - English, Irish, Scots and Welsh - are made more intelligible if they are seen, throughout the last two thousand years, within a general British Isles context and in terms of a complex of interacting cultures. Kearney's wide-ranging survey is a challenge to traditional assumptions about what constitutes national history and, in Christopher Hill's words, 'should be widely used to educate those who think they know about British history when in fact they know only English history.'

Morton, A.L.
A People's History of England
Lawrence & Wishart pbk £9.99
0853157235
Morton's classic work - a bold attempt to examine the main outlines and major turning points in English history from the perspective of ordinary people - has been continuously in print for more than fifty years. At the time it was written it was a pioneering example of history seen from the viewpoint of the ruled rather than that of the rulers. Many historians have followed in Morton's footsteps but, as Eric Hobsbawm noted, 'nobody since has written a single-volume history to compare with it.'

Reproduced from the *Illustrated History of Europe* *(Weidenfeld & Nicolson)*.

Palmer, Alan (ed)
Pimlico Chronology of British History
Pimlico pbk £14.00
0712673318

This is an invaluable reference work for students, for teachers and for anyone with more than a passing interest in history. Into its 584 pages is crammed essential information on all aspects of British history from prehistoric times to the end of 1995. In the form of time-charts and tables, 12,000 individual events are described, dated and classified under one of nine broad headings, from science and invention to literature and scholarship. The book also includes the names of 10,000 individuals who have made their mark on British history, maps which cover periods from Roman Britain to the Second World War, and invaluable demographic and economic statistics.

Porter, Roy
London: A Social History
Penguin pbk £15.00
014010593X

Roy Porter is one of the most prolific and talented historians of his generation and this is a vivid and enlightening narrative history of one of the world's greatest cities. Cleverly interweaving facts and statistics with the more impressionistic evidence of diarists like Pepys and Boswell, novelists like Fielding and Dickens and pioneering social researchers like Mayhew, Porter has produced a book which gives shape and coherence to the whole sweep of London's history. Porter's commitment to his subject and love of London are evident throughout, perhaps most obviously in his concluding, savage indictment of recent Tory policies and their impact on the city.

Porter, Roy
A Social History of Madness
Phoenix pbk £8.99
1857995023

Roy Porter has constructed a minutely detailed, fascinating and illuminating account of the writings of mad people in history. Although the preservation of necessary documents means inevitably that he addresses the writings of a sub-group, namely famous mad people, this does not detract from the insights to be gained from this book. Roy Porter became interested in the notion of madness reflecting the perceived 'sane' world - like children mimicking grown-ups - but does not attempt to psychoanalyse 'true' or subconscious meaning in the texts he examines. Despite the almost inevitable presence of the likes of Freud in the text, this is, as it claims, a social not a psychological history. However much the insane individual distorts the value systems and beliefs and social practices of those around them, they still form a fascinating reflection of the times in which they lived, and a revealing counterpart to those 'sane' individuals who deemed them mad. Roy Porter is a witty and erudite guide through this anthology of case histories, and his approach is both absorbing and persuasive.

Samuel, Raphael
Theatres of Memory
Verso pbk £13.95
1859840779

Critics of the heritage industry deplore our current obsession with the past and argue that it represents not a return to tradition but a symptom of national decay and a distortion of history to meet commercial demands. In this challenging book Samuel, one of the founders of History Workshop, argues that interest in the past shown by ordinary people should not be smugly dismissed by professional historians and that we live in an expanding historical culture, one which is more democratic than earlier versions of the national past, and one more open to the claims of minorities.

Strong, Roy
The Story of Britain
Hutchinson hbk £35.00
1856810992
'A country which is ignorant of its past loses its identity.' So Sir Roy Strong writes in this well-illustrated and well-produced one-volume history of Britain. Published at a time when history is a subject of enormous debate, this continuous narrative tells the story of Britain in chapters that give life and meaning to every period from the earliest Celtic times to the present day.

Thomas, Keith
Man and the Natural World
Penguin pbk £9.99
0140146865
This is an encyclopaedic study of man's relationship to animals and plants in this country and of the dramatic changes which occurred, between 1500 and 1800, in the way people of all social classes perceived and classified the natural world around them. As a result of these changes, Keith Thomas argues, long-established dogmas about man's position in nature were abandoned and our relationship with other species were redefined. In these centuries of change lie the origins of our own intense interest in the natural world and our own heightened anxieties about the threat we offer to it. Drawing on a rich array of historical and literary evidence, Thomas covers topics as diverse as the gradual separation of popular and learned views of the natural world, the development of pet-keeping, and the history of vegetarianism in a brilliantly original and entertaining book.

Trevelyan, G.M.
English Social History
Penguin pbk £9.99
0140233229
A Shortened History of England
Penguin pbk £8.99
0140233237
Trevelyan (1876 -1962) came from what was almost a dynasty of historians - his father wrote prolifically about eighteenth century politics and he was the great-nephew of Lord Macaulay - and was appointed Regius professor of modern history at Cambridge in 1927. He wrote widely on subjects as diverse as Garibaldi's campaigns in Italy and the England of Queen Anne and, although his style of history writing is very outmoded, *A Shortened History of England* and his nostalgic account of six hundred years of *English Social History* remain in print and continue to find a readership.

Reproduced from *The Oxford Illustrated History of Tudor and Stuart Britain* (Oxford).

How Many Londons?

by Roy Porter

The author of the highly-acclaimed London: A Social History, reflects on 2000 years of the nation's capital

Dickens' title *A Tale of Two Cities* might be thought to apply perfectly well to the history of London alone. Administratively speaking, London grew up as two separate entities, the settlement founded by the Romans in 43 A.D. which was later to be known as the City of London, and, a couple of miles to the west, the City of Westminster, which was to become the focus of the Court, Parliament and in some measure the Church. And, alongside the official twin cities, we should imagine London as being rather as Julius Caesar described Gaul: a whole, divided into three parts. Historically, London is best viewed not as two distinct cities, but as a single metropolis with three different elements: the City, Westminster and the suburbs.

London's history must be understood as a whole. It has evolved organically - it was a 'polypus.....a vast irregular growth', thought the pioneering twentieth century urban planner, Patrick Geddes, 'perhaps likest to the spreading of a great coral reef.' It has expanded and survived thanks to its own inner energies. Unlike certain cities - for instance, modern Brasilia - London has never been an artificial colony, planted by the diktat of some potentate to serve the purposes of government, defence or prestige. Rather it grew of its own accord, at some basic level out of the intrinsic geographical and economic logic of its own location, situated as it is at the lowest point where the Thames could readily be forded and bridged, furnishing a convenient, commercial nucleus from which trade could be conducted with the Continent.

This explains why early London thrived. By around 200 A.D. the walled city that the Romans had built on the north bank of the Thames supported a population of up to 30,000. In due course the Romans left and Londinium fell into decay. But, from around the eighth century, the Anglo-Saxon rulers redeveloped it as a bulwark against the marauding Vikings and the city grew in significance as trade revived with the Low Countries and France.

After the Norman Conquest in 1066, William I made London his capital, building the White Tower and refortifying the walls. And during the medieval centuries the city of London, clustering north of its bridge between St. Paul's and the Tower, expanded as a mighty centre of trade and manufactures, with a busy port and thriving guilds.

The sixteenth and seventeenth centuries brought astonishing growth. Around 50,000 people were living there in 1500, but, by the time of the accession of Charles II in 1660, London's population had increased at least tenfold. Before 1800 London had long overtaken Paris to become Europe's biggest city, with a population approaching one million.

Unlike Paris, London united in one single settlement all the functions associated with urban life. It was Britain's largest manufacturing centre; its waterfront had become easily the most dynamic port in the world. Especially after the founding of the Bank of England (1694), London also became a world centre of finance. But it was equally a mecca of fashion, consumption, and the entertainment and communications industries.

London mushroomed in the nineteenth century. In 1800 one in ten inhabitants of England and Wales dwelt in the metropolis; by 1900 that fraction had leapt to a breathtaking one in five. Between 1890 and 1940, Greater London grew from 5,368,000 to 8,700,000 people. Cheap building land was available and nineteenth-century builders enjoyed a brisk demand for different sorts of residences: some catering for the rich in new inner areas like Belgravia and Kensington; some for the middle classes in suburban districts like Islington and Camden Town; and others for the respectable labouring poor, in the East End of town and beyond the docks in Hackney and Poplar, West Ham and East Ham.

As well as feeding its citizens, London also provided them with work. Migrants flooded in because there were always plenty of openings - in the manufacturing trades, food-processing, liquor-distilling, leather-making, furniture-making; in the clothing industry where the 'sweat-shop system' prevailed; in the distributive trades and, not least ,domestic service.

Growing population, economic prosperity and a more sophisticated communications network demanded, and finally yielded, new structures of municipal government. For a long time London had been a patchwork of authorities left over from the Middle Ages, including the City Corporation. Finally in 1889 there emerged the London County Council (LCC), perhaps the first unified government the town had enjoyed since it had been Londinium; in 1965 that was replaced by the Greater London Council (GLC), abolished in 1986 by Margaret Thatcher. By then, London had extended so far it was difficult to say where it stopped: out towards Brighton, Reading, Northampton and Southend. This modern decanting of town into the countryside may be the late twentieth-century solution to the problem of the decay of the inner city and the obsolescence of town life as traditionally known, or it may be a problem in itself, which it will be left for the twenty-first century to solve.

Pre-Roman & Roman Britain

Breeze, David & Dobson, Brian
Hadrian's Wall
Penguin pbk £8.99
0140135499

Begun in the time of the Emperor Hadrian, the Wall was one of the most elaborate building projects undertaken by the Romans and what remains of the 74 mile stretch from Wallsend to Bowness-on-Solway, together with the accompanying forts and buildings, is an indication of their engineering skill. The wall was intended to mark the boundary of the Roman world and to keep out hostile tribes to the North. It was abandoned when the legions left in the 5th century. This revised edition of a standard work is an ideal introduction to the history and archaeology of the Wall.

Caesar, Julius
(102/100 - 44 B.C.)
Conquest of Gaul
Penguin pbk £6.99
0140444335

As well as being a politician and general of genius, Caesar was a writer possessed of considerable lucidity and narrative skill. His own account of his campaigns includes a description of his incursions into Britain in 55-54 B.C. and a fascinating picture of the customs of the early Britons.

Chadwick, Nora
The Celts
Penguin pbk £7.99
0140250743

The product of a lifetime of research in the field, this book is a standard history of the Celts in Britain and their culture from their arrival in the 8th century B.C., through the period in which they occupied the greater part of the British Isles, to the centuries in which, pressurised first by the Romans and then by the Saxon invaders, they were pushed to the margins. Chapters on Celtic art and literature, on mythology and the Celtic adoption of Christianity complement chapters on the origins and development of the Celtic kingdoms in this lucid account.

Chippindale, Christopher
Stonehenge Complete
Thames & Hudson pbk £12.95
0500277508

A revised edition of a comprehensive introduction to its subject, this book presents both the Stonehenge that modern archaeological scholarship has revealed and the Stonehenge that previous ages have imagined and created, from the antiquary John Aubrey in the 17th century to visitors in the Victorian era and beyond. Some of the more inventive theories of the purpose of the monument, both present and historical, are also reviewed.

Frere, Sheppard
Britannia
Pimlico pbk £15.00
071265027X

Since its first publication in the sixties, Sheppard Frere's book has established itself as the most lucid and wide-ranging introduction to its subject. *Britannia* provides a compelling narrative history, from Caesar's first sight of Dover in 55 B. C. to the province's separation from Rome in A.D. 410. It also includes separate chapters on individual topics such as the administration of the province, the role of the army, life in the towns the Romans created and the trade and industry that developed through the centuries. Frere, a distinguished archaeologist, has succeeded admirably in weaving together the information produced by decades of excavation of Roman sites and the evidence to be found in texts and inscriptions, to produce a convincing picture of life in Britain under Roman rule.

Peddie, John
Conquest : The Roman Invasion of Britain
Sutton pbk £10.99
0862998697

John Peddie, author of a successful book on Roman military organisation, is a retired infantry soldier and brings his military experience to bear in this innovative reappraisal of the Claudian invasion of Britain. Peddie's argument that Roman tactics were largely dictated by the logistical demands of the invasion is a compelling one and his further suggestions of reasons behind the apparently unnecessary diversion of troops to the West Country and the difficulties created by Caractacus' guerrilla campaign are also thought-provoking.

Salway, Peter
Roman Britain
Oxford UP pbk £12.99
0192851438

This volume in the Oxford History of England is one of the few indispensable works on the period. Salway draws together literary sources and the evidence provided by the huge advances in Romano-British archaeology in the last few decades to create a narrative that is simultaneously very learned and very access-ible. Beginning with Caesar's expeditions across the Channel, Salway carries the reader through the Claudian invasion a century later, through the consolidation of Roman power under such generals and governors as Suetonius Paulinus and Agricola, through several centuries of Roman rule in the province, to the collapse of imperial rule in the early 5th century A.D. and the first barbarian incursions into the province. This is an authorita-tive account of a province that was not only an integral part of the Roman Empire but also possessed of its own distinctive character.

Tacitus (c. 55 - 117 A.D.)
Agricola/Germania
Penguin pbk £6.99
0140442413

Tacitus was probably Imperial Rome's greatest historian. His monograph in praise of his father-in-law, the general Agricola, includes much about the latter's achievements in Roman Britain and details of the customs of the tribes ruled by the Romans.

Reproduced from the *Illustrated History of Europe* (Weidenfeld & Nicolson).

Ireland, S.
Roman Britain
Routledge pbk £14.99
0415131340

The most comprehensive and exhaustive collection of literary, numismatic and epigraphic evidence of the Roman conquest and settlement of Britain readily available, this is an essential volume for anyone seriously interested in the period. The predominantly military material is sorted under chronological headings for easy reference and the sourcebook also includes an introduction to the geography and people of Britain before the invasion of 43 A.D. and chapters devoted to commerce and religion in Roman Britain. This is an invaluable record of surviving evidence from this formative period of our history.

Anglo-Saxon Britain

Alcock, Leslie
Arthur's Britain
Penguin pbk £9.99
0140136053
Leslie Alcock is the archaeologist who conducted a well-known excavation of Cadbury Castle in Somerset in the late sixties, a site which had long been identified with Arthur's legendary court at Camelot. His book, written at the time of his involvement in the Cadbury Castle dig, is an attempt to sift history from myth in the period between A.D. 367, in which the first barbarian attack on Roman Britain took place, and A.D. 634, which saw the last great British counterattack against the Anglo-Saxon invaders. It is also an attempt to construct a convincing picture of the society in which Arthur, if he was an historical figure, would have fought his rearguard actions against the invaders. This new edition includes an expanded bibliography to take account of the upsurge in work on the period in the last twenty years.

Bede (673 - 735)
Ecclesiastical History of the English People
Penguin pbk £8.99
014044565X
Bede spent most of his life working as a scholar and teacher in the monastery at Jarrow in Northumberland. His most famous work is a Latin history of the English people, beginning with Caesar's invasion and ending with a description of the state of the nation in 731, the year in which it was finished.

Campbell, James
The Anglo-Saxons
Penguin pbk £15.00
0140143955
From the end of Roman rule to the Battle of Hastings, a period of six and a half centuries, the Anglo-Saxons dominated England. Many of the religious, administrative and cultural achievements of later centuries have their foundation in the Anglo- Saxon period and the legacy of this gifted and creative people is with us today. This large format, beautifully illustrated book makes an excellent introduction to Anglo-Saxon history, dispelling the myth that the Anglo-Saxon centuries were simply a barbarous prelude to better things.

Dunning, Robert
Arthur : The King in the West
Sutton pbk £9.99
0750909943
The question, 'Did Arthur really exist?' is not a simple one to answer and the debate continues about which, if any, elements in the legend have their foundation in historical fact. Dunning's contribution to the debate is an accessible book examining the links between the legends and specific sites in the West Country, most notably the abbey at Glastonbury and the Somerset hillfort of South Cadbury. Dunning makes clear the extent to which the legends are deep-rooted in the West, unravelling the way in which the Abbey of Glastonbury created the potent combination of a popular hero and the mystery of the Grail, allied it to the abbey's own fortunes, and thus kept the foundation at the forefront of English monasticism.

Ellis, Peter Berresford
The Celtic Empire
Constable pbk £10.95
0094732604

The Celts were the first European people north of the Alps to emerge into recorded history and, at one time, they dominated the continent from Ireland in the west to Turkey in the east, from Belgium in the north to Spain and Italy in the south. Berresford Ellis, the author of several highly regarded works on Celtic culture, has written a lucid account of a thousand years of Celtic history, in which a Celtic Empire developed although it was an empire without an emperor and without a central government. Rather it was made up of independent tribes who nonetheless succeeded in imposing their own distinctive culture and values on other peoples.

Geoffrey of Monmouth (d. 1155)
History of the Kings of Britain
Penguin pbk £6.99
0140441700

Geoffrey of Monmouth was a Benedictine monk whose work purported to give a history of those kings who had ruled in Britain from the great-grandson of Aeneas, Brutus, to Cadwallader in the 7th Century A.D., giving particular emphasis to the exploits of King Arthur. *The History of the Kings of Britain* is virtually worthless as a record of genuine historical facts but the liveliness of its style and narrative gave much impetus to the popularity of Arthurian legend.

Morris, John
The Age of Arthur
Phoenix pbk £12.99
1857992865

This is the classic account of a period in Britain's history which is shrouded in myth and mystery and for which documentation and archaeological evidence are equally scanty. John Morris was an historian who was vastly learned in the surviving evidence and this history of the centuries from 350 to 650, first published in the seventies, is fully deserving of this recent reissue. In the first half of the book he produces a narrative which makes sense for the general reader of these confusing centuries and which explains convincingly the transition from Roman Britain to an island in which the recognisable outlines of future English, Welsh, Scottish and Irish nations can be traced. In the second half he provides a broad analysis of the religious, economic and social history of the period.

Myres, J. N. L.
The English Settlements
Oxford UP pbk £8.99
0192822357

Published as part of the Oxford History of England, Myres' book is a comprehensive account of the dark ages of English history between the departure of the Roman legions in the early fifth century and the emergence of the Anglo-Saxon kingdoms two centuries later. Myres investigates closely the nature of the meagre evidence - literary, archaeological and toponymic - on which the historian has to draw but uses that evidence to great effect in a study which remains an invaluable introduction to the period.

Reproduced from the *Illustrated History of Europe* (Weidenfeld & Nicolson).

Powell, T.G.E.
The Celts
Thames & Hudson pbk £7.95
0500272751

The Celts were the first great nation north of the Alps whose name we know. Powell's book on them was first published in 1958 and rapidly established itself as one of the best introductions to its subject. More than twenty years later a new edition was prepared by Stuart Piggott and further illustration was added to what was already a highly-illustrated text. It is a tribute to the depth of Powell's scholarship that, despite the advances made in Celtic studies recently, his account of the rich variety of Celtic life and culture, across the whole of Europe and across many centuries, can still be highly recommended.

Stenton, Frank
Anglo-Saxon England
Oxford UP pbk £11.99
0192822373

Stenton's book, although published many years ago, remains a valuable introduction to the period it covers. He gives a lucid account of the gradual unification of England, begun by the kings of Mercia and continued by the kings of Wessex, most notably Alfred and Athelstan. He also traces the development of English society and its administrative structure from the oldest Anglo-Saxon laws to the establishment by the Normans of their own variant of feudalism.

Swanton, Michael (ed)
The Anglo-Saxon Chronicle
Dent pbk £5.99
0460876325

The Anglo-Saxon Chronicle, first brought together in the reign of Alfred the Great, and afterwards continued in a number of different versions written at different monasteries, is the main source for events and chronology in the period between the 5th and 11th centuries. The information it provides is of varying degrees of reliability but it gives a vivid and lively picture of Anglo-Saxon England.

Medieval England

Allmand, Christopher
The Hundred Years' War
Cambridge UP pbk £10.95
0521319234

Allmand's compact study of the long period of conflict between France and England known as the Hundred Years' War includes both a narrative outline of events and the major battles - Crécy, Poitiers, Agincourt - and an analysis of the social and economic effects in both countries. The book is one of a series of Cambridge Medieval Textbooks, intended primarily for the student. However the interested general reader will find that it offers new insights into its particular subject and into the general history of warfare in medieval times.

Chibnall, Marjorie
Anglo-Norman England
Blackwell pbk £13.99
0631154396

This is the most up-to-date and comprehensive account available of the century of interaction between peoples and cultures following the Norman Conquest and the best-known date in English history. Chibnall makes clear the complexities which lie behind the old myths of free and equal Englishmen corrupted by the Norman yoke and provides a convincing account of the development of feudalism in this country. She shows how Norman lords came to accept old English traditions as part of their own heritage, how the invading warriors of the conquest were transformed into the knights of the shires and how, in general, an Anglo-Norman society and culture emerged.

Chrimes etc
Fifteenth Century England
Sutton pbk £9.99
0750909234

This collection of essays, first published in 1972, provides a series of insights for the student of the 15th century into many of the issues and controversies that historians of the period are still debating. The essays range from Charles Ross on the reign of Edward IV to a study of the nobility and gentry, from S. B. Chrimes on Henry VII to R. A. Griffith's groundbreaking survey of Wales and the Marches.

Coss, Peter
The Knight in Medieval England
Sutton pbk £9.99
075090996X

Knight service - the military service owed to a lord in return for land held from that lord - was one of the cornerstones of medieval society and the men who performed that service were important members of society. Coss's illustrated survey looks at the origins and evolution of knighthood in England in late Saxon and early Norman times through to the idealized portraits of knightly chivalry presented by Chaucer and his contemporaries and beyond, paying particular attention to the details of knightly practice -what the knight did - and to the knight's role in society.

Hibbert, Christopher
Agincourt
Windrush Press pbk £9.99
0900075295

This is a concise and compelling account of one of the great successes of English arms in which the archers and men at arms of Henry V's army defeated a much larger French force. Hibbert explores the background to the conflict, traces the English expedition's journey across the Channel and across northern France and gives a detailed description of the battle itself. This is a reprint of a book first published in the sixties and is one of a series of Great Battles brought back into print by Windrush Press.

Keen, Maurice
England in the Later Middle Ages
Routledge pbk £15.99
0415027837

This is a political history of England in the two difficult centuries between 1290 and 1485, centuries which saw the deposition of Edward II, Henry IV's usurpation of Richard II's throne, Henry V's wars of conquest in France and the Wars of the Roses. In addition, the country suffered the demographic catastrophe of

the Black Death and witnessed the Peasants' Revolt, possibly the most significant popular rebellion in English history. Keen's admirable study balances narrative history with discursive chapters on the social, religious and intellectual developments of the period.

Lander, J. R
The Wars of the Roses
Sutton pbk £9.99
0750900180

The Wars of the Roses were a series of interconnected struggles for possession of the English crown in the period between the 1450s and the 1480s. The inadequacies of Henry VI led ambitious magnates into armed conflict and, after Edward IV had appeared to consolidate his power through victory at the Battle of Towton in 1461, conflict was renewed when Warwick the Kingmaker revitalised the Lancastrian cause by allying himself with Margaret of Anjou, the wife of Henry VI. A third period of turmoil followed Richard III's accession to the throne, ending with Henry Tudor's victory at Bosworth and Richard's death. Lander's account of these troubled times, drawing as far as possible on contemporary records, is one of the most succinct and comprehensible surveys of its subject.

McKisack, May
The Fourteenth Century
Oxford UP pbk £9.99
0192852507

The fourteenth century was a difficult and turbulent period in English history, a century in which two monarchs were murdered by rivals for the throne, in which perhaps half the population was wiped out by the Black Death and by famine, and more lost their lives through war with Scotland and with France. It was also a period of great creativity - the first flowering of vernacular literature culminated in the work of Chaucer - and developments occurred in the parliamentary, administrative and legal systems which shaped them for centuries to come. First published in 1959, this classic account retains its position as the ideal introduction to the period for students and the general reader.

illustrative, demonstrating the hold that the preoccupation with sudden death continued to have on the imaginations of late medieval men and women.

Pollard, A.J.
Richard III and the Princes in the Tower
Sutton pbk £14.99
0750903546

Was Richard III a tyrant and the murderer of his innocent nephews? Or was he an enlightened prince who has been outrageously maligned by successive generations of propagandists, dramatists and historians? While acknowledging the difficulty of establishing 'the truth' in the light of the paucity of the surviving evidence and the way the original events have been subsumed by later literary versions, Pollard gives his own lively account of Richard's life and reign and of the disappearance of the princes. One of the book's chief attractions is its rich and imaginative use of manuscript illustrations and contemporary engravings and documents.

Powicke, Maurice
The Thirteenth Century
Oxford UP pbk £11.99
0192852493

Powicke's classic account of the long reigns of Henry III and

Davis, Norman (ed)
The Paston Letters
Oxford UP pbk £4.99
0192816152

A selection, in modernised spelling, of the letters written by a prosperous Norfolk family living through the upheaval, unrest and casual violence of 15th century England. The letters reveal much fascinating detail of the political and social disorder produced by the Wars of the Roses and the impact this disorder had on several generations of one family. They also include a great deal of information about the domestic conditions of a well-to-do, late medieval household.

Platt, Colin
King Death
UCL Press pbk £12.95
1857283147

Subtitled *The Black Death and its Aftermath in late-medieval England,* this book is a powerful and well-written account of what it was like to live in a society in which the plague was a continually threatening presence. The plague affected all levels of society, from serf to aristocrat, and Platt examines the social and economic consequences of the decline in population. The book presents a wide range of evidence, documentary and

Edward I underlines the formative influence these years had on the development of English history. Henry's ineffectuality as a ruler and the challenge to his authority by Simon de Montfort led to the summoning of the most important of early English parliaments. Meanwhile the long campaigns by Edward to subdue the Welsh and the Scots led to a radical readjustment of the nation's borders. Powicke's highly detailed but readable narrative of the two reigns addresses these and many other issues, examines the involvement of both kings with the Crusades and with France, and sets the political and social developments within a wider European context.

Reproduced from the *Illustrated History of Europe* (Weidenfeld & Nicolson).

Richard III and the Wars of the Roses

A brief look at some more titles on the subject

There are several excellent one-volume surveys of the Wars of the Roses available to the non-specialist reader and these are reviewed in the section of this guide on Medieval England. There are also a number of other studies targeted at particular audiences. John Warren's **The Wars of the Roses and the Yorkist Kings** (Arnold 0340611146 £5.99) is one of a series, Access to History, which is designed to meet the needs of sixth-form students and provides a concise analysis of the central issues and historical interpretation of them. Two books written and edited by A.J. Pollard, both called **The Wars of the Roses** and both published by Macmillan, provide more detailed examination of the conflict. The first, in a series called Problems in Focus (Macmillan 0333601661 £13.50), is a collection of essays by distinguished medievalists which cover topics from the origins of the wars to their economic effects. The second title, in the British History in Perspective series, is Pollard's own closely argued study of the Wars as a fundamental crisis in the late-medieval political order. Philip Haigh's **The Military Campaigns of the Wars of the Roses** (Sutton 0750914300 £10.99) places a specific emphasis on the strategy and tactics employed in the fifteen battles of the wars.

Sutton, who publish a range of titles on medieval history, produce a number that focus on particular battles. A.W. Boardman's **The Battle of Towton** (Sutton 0750912456 £10.99) is the first ever comprehensive account of the conflict which gave Edward IV the throne and Philip Haigh's **The Battle of Wakefield** (Sutton 0750913428 £18.99) investigates a significant engagement which has been relatively neglected by other historians. Bosworth is, of course, the battle of the Wars which nearly everybody remembers and Michael Bennett's **The Battle of Bosworth** (Sutton 0862994268 £10.99) is a well-illustrated, well-written account of the meeting between Richard III and Henry Tudor.

If Bosworth is the battle that everyone remembers then that is largely because of the fact that it proved the downfall of Richard III and, five hundred years after his death, he remains the most controversial of all English monarchs. Was he a bloodthirsty tyrant who murdered his own nephews in his lust for power? Or was he a capable and effective monarch maligned by the propaganda of those who overthrew him? Yale University Press publish an edition of the work which could be said to have initiated the damning of Richard's character, **The History of King Richard III by Sir Thomas More** (Yale UP 0300019254 £9.95). **The Betrayal of Richard III** (Sutton 086299778X £7.99) is a classic survey of Richard's life and times which examines the contemporary evidence for his reign and traces the origins of the traditional picture of him as murderous monster. A more specialist view of Richard and his reign is contained in **Richard III : A Study of Service** (Cambridge UP 0521407265 £14.95) edited by Rosemary Horrox which endeavours to correct the imbalance created by historians' concentration on the monarch's character through an examination of royal government in the period and the role of the king's servants. **Good King Richard?** (Constable 0094688400 £10.95) by Jeremy Potter is a readable account of the king's life and his reputation over five hundred years. The best modern, scholarly biography is by Charles Ross - **Richard III** (University of California Press 0520050754 £11.50). The wealth of material on Richard may not mean that the truth about his character and deeds will ever be unarguably decided but it does mean that the caricatured villain portrayed by Shakespeare has been relegated to the realm of drama rather than history.

Ross, Charles
The Wars of the Roses
Thames & Hudson pbk £7.95
050027407X

The years of warfare and
upheaval brought about by 'the
division and dissension of the
renowned houses of Lancaster
and York', years which saw the
violent deaths of three kings,
were presented for several
centuries, largely as a consequence of Tudor propaganda
and Shakespearean drama, as
a period of bloody horrors and
unmitigated evils from which
England was only rescued by
the emergence of Henry Tudor
from obscurity and exile to
defeat Richard III at Bosworth.
Some modern scholars have
tended to downplay the importance of the Wars of the Roses.
For most English people, they
argue, the wars had little relevance and the problems which
undoubtedly afflicted fifteenth
century society were neither
greatly exacerbated nor greatly
alleviated by them. This book,
highly illustrated and lucidly
written, is an attempt by one
distinguished historian to
provide an analysis of the Wars
that neither overestimates their
importance but gives an
accurate assessment
of their impact on English
people and English society.

Weir, Alison
**Lancaster and York:
The Wars of the Roses**
Arrow pbk £8.99
0099663511

The conflict between the two
houses of Lancaster and York,
a bloody series of battles for
the throne, scarred England
in the years between 1455 and
1487, brought about the downfall of both houses and paved
the way for the emergence of
the Tudor dynasty. Alison Weir's
gripping account of this struggle
focuses on the personalities
involved - the pious but ineffec-
tual Henry VI whose failures as a
ruler ensured decades of political
chaos, Henry's rival Richard
Plantaganet, Duke of York, and
Henry's wife, Margaret of Anjou,
strong where Henry was weak,
who was the most effective
champion of her husband's
cause.

Reproduced from the *Oxford Illustrated
History of Medieval Europe* (Oxford).

Weir, Alison
The Princes in the Tower
Pimlico pbk £8.99
0712673792

The story of the deaths of
the boy-king Edward V and his
younger brother Richard, Duke
of York, while they were lodged
in the Tower of London, is one
of the best-known episodes in
English history and much ink
has been spilled in efforts to
unearth the truth about the
deaths. Many historians have
pointed accusing fingers at the
boys' uncle, Richard III. Yet
societies have been formed to
defend what members believe
to be his unfairly besmirched
reputation. Alison Weir, in this
lucid and absorbing book, has
re-examined all the evidence
and reconstructs the political
events that led to the deaths.
She makes a convincing case
for her interpretation of how,
why and by whose order the
princes died.

The Tudor Age

Davis, C. S. L.
Peace, Print and Protestantism
Fontana pbk £8.99
000686354X

Davies highlights three themes in this introduction to the period of English history between 1450, when the country was sliding into the anarchy of the Wars of the Roses, and 1558, the year of Elizabeth's accession to the throne of a nation that, despite change and uncertainty, had enjoyed more than seventy years of peace. The creation of this precarious peace is one of his themes. The others are the revolution in the dissemination of knowledge brought about by the invention of printing and the gradual appearance of a radical new religious conscious-ness. The book's emphasis is on political history and on the changes wrought by chance and contingency and by the personalities, weak and strong, of successive monarchs.

Duffy, Eamon
The Stripping of the Altars
Yale UP £11.99
0300060769

Historians have often assumed that the pre-Reformation church in this country was corrupt and unpopular and that the Reformation itself was an expression of the popular will as much as an autocrat's dynastic needs. In this impressive and scholarly work, Duffy demon-strates that this was not the case and illustrates the extent to which late medieval Catholicism enjoyed popular support. The Reformation, in Duffy's view, was imposed from above on a populace unwilling to relinquish its customary rites and ceremonies. His detailed examination of the impact of the Reformation at parish level reveals the world which was destroyed and provides the reader with a very different perspective on the period.

Elton, G. R.
England Under the Tudors
Routledge pbk £13.99

First published in 1954, and revised in 1991, this remains one of the best introductions to Tudor history available, both for the student and the general reader. Although necessarily examining other areas as well,

Elton's chief interest, as he wrote in the preface to the original edition, 'is the condition, reconstruction and gradual moulding of a state - the history of a nation and its leaders in political action and therefore the history of govern-ment in its widest sense.' One of these leaders is Thomas Cromwell whom Elton, contrary to most earlier opinion, champions as a statesman who established far-reaching administrative procedures. Elton's independence and incisiveness as an historian are evident throughout a text that is lucid, witty and readable.

Fraser, Antonia
Mary, Queen of Scots
Mandarin pbk £7.99
0749301082
Mary Queen of Scots has been the focus of an extraordinary amount of romantic historical attention in the four hundred years since her execution at Fotheringhay Castle in Northamptonshire. Antonia Fraser's biography, tracing Mary's story from her birth and accession to the Scottish throne at the age of six days, through

her unfortunate marriages to the French Dauphin and to Lord Darnley, to her long imprisonment by her cousin Elizabeth I, is an attempt to untangle the truth about this ill-fated monarch from the accretions of the myth.

Fraser, Antonia
The Six Wives of Henry VIII
Arrow pbk £8.99
0099529815

'Divorced, beheaded, died ; divorced, beheaded, survived.' As this mnemonic verse, known to generations of schoolchildren, suggests, the six women who suffered the unenviable fate of becoming one of Henry VIII's wives are remembered not for their lives but for the way their lives (and marriages) ended. Antonia Fraser's composite biography, written in her characteristically readable style, details the story of each wife and reveals the individual characters of the women who were more than just the unwilling victims of Henry's dynastic ambition to produce a male heir.

Griffiths, Ralph & Thomas, Roger
The Making of the Tudor Dynasty
Sutton pbk £9.99
0862994276

Much has been written about the Tudor monarchs - from Henry VII to Elizabeth - but this well researched book, another in Sutton's Illustrated Paperback series, is one of the few to delve into the origins of the Tudor family and to trace the story of its fluctuating fortunes in the centuries before Bosworth. From its beginnings in North Wales in the service of the princes of Gwynedd, Griffiths and Thomas follow the family in its involvement with the rebellion of Owen Glyndwr, the marriage of Owen Tudor to the widow of Henry V and the active participation of Jasper and Henry Tudor in the struggles between Lancastrians and Yorkists.

Guy, John
Tudor England
Oxford UP pbk £8.99
0192852132

Published in 1988, this was the first comprehensive history of Tudor England for more than thirty years. Guy's intention was to write a clear narrative account of the period between the advent of the Tudors in the 1460s and the death of Elizabeth and in this he succeeds triumphantly. The book, based on the most thorough knowledge of the sources and literature, chronicles the far-reaching changes in government and the Reformation of the Church which Tudor England witnessed in the years after Henry VII's capture of the crown at Bosworth. An indispensable work for anyone interested in the period.

Hale, John
England and the Italian Renaissance
Fontana pbk £8.99
0006863477

This was the first book by John Hale, one of Britain's leading historians of the Renaissance, and was originally published in 1954. It remains a pioneering study of Anglo-Italian cultural relations and succeeds in illumi-

Reproduced from *The Oxford Illustrated History of Tudor and Stuart Britain* (Oxford).

nating both the Renaissance itself and the responses of English admirers from William Thomas, who published his *Historie of Italie* in 1549, to the Victorian scholar John Addington Symonds. It does so, as Nicholas Penny writes in a new introduction to this edition, 'deftly, engagingly and with great learning.'

Hibbert, Christopher
The Virgin Queen
Penguin pbk £7.99
0140087389

During her reign, a cult developed around the figure of Elizabeth I, praised by courtiers and poets for her wit, her beauty and her statecraft - the Virgin Queen presiding over a new golden age. Hibbert's biography of the queen is detailed and revealing and, while based on sound scholarship and knowledge, is a colourful portrait of a rich and interesting personality.

Loades, David
Henry VIII and His Queens
Sutton pbk £10.99
0750912472

Too often the six queens of Henry VIII are seen as one-dimensional and cardboard figures, unwitting participants in a bizarre and bloody royal soap opera. David Loades retells the well-known story of Henry's wives from a political perspective, demonstrating clearly the individuality of those concerned and the role each wife played in the wider politics of Henry's reign.

Marius, Richard
Thomas More
Weidenfeld pbk £12.99
0297813862

Saint, humanist, author of the enigmatic fable *Utopia*, politician and ultimately martyr to the cause of individual conscience, More was one of the most complex and fascinating figures of the Tudor period. In a much-acclaimed biography Marius throws light on the inner conflicts of a man forced, through political circumstance and despite his own strenuous efforts to avoid it, into a confrontation with Henry VIII over the King's assertion of royal supremacy, a confrontation that led inexorably to More's fall from favour, trial and eventual execution.

Mattingly, Garret
The Defeat of the Spanish Armada
Penguin pbk £7.99
0140124136

The Spanish Armada of 1588 and the heroic defence of English waters by the likes of Sir Francis Drake and Sir John Hawkins provides one of the great myths of English history and has done so since the propagandists of Elizabethan England first seized upon the victory. Mattingly's classic account reveals the complex realities behind the myth - the impossible demands made upon the Spanish commander Medina Sidonia and his fleet in the context of 16th century naval warfare, the importance of weather conditions in influencing the outcome and the extent to which fortune favoured the English.

Ridley, Jasper
The Tudor Age
Constable pbk £12.95
0094728704

The Tudor Age began on the 7th August 1485 when Henry Tudor, Earl of Richmond, landed at Milford Haven with 2000 soldiers, intent on wresting the English throne from Richard III, and ended on the 24th March 1603 with the death of Elizabeth I after a reign of forty five years. It was an age of splendour and of squalor and Jasper Ridley captures both in this large format, splendidly illustrated social history of the period. In a succession of vividly written chapters he evokes the costume and fashion, the sports and pastimes, the furniture and food, the entire tapestry of the social life of this important period in English history.

Salgado, Gamini
The Elizabethan Underworld
Sutton pbk £9.99
0750909765
Illustrated throughout with
woodcuts of the period, this
lively survey recreates the reality
of life on the streets of London
during the sixteenth century.
Beginning with a snapshot of
the 'conycatchers' and their
tricks, the book moves on to an
in-depth portrait of the sexual
underworld of the stews; the
swindles and reality of the
various practitioners of the black
arts; and the wandering bands of
beggars, pedlars, gypsies and
actors. The book also includes
a careful description of the
criminal justice system of the day
and a glossary of Elizabethan
thieves' cant which allows the
reader to distinguish his dell
from his doxy. Salgado's work
is an essential companion to
realities often reflected in the
work of Shakespeare and other
contemporary dramatists.

Weir, Alison
The Six Wives of Henry VIII
Pimlico pbk £8.99
0712673849
A composite biography of the
six women who were married
to the Tudor monarch, this book
is highly readable as well as
thoroughly researched. Writing
on individuals as different as the
pious and principled Katherine
of Aragon, the allegedly promis-
cuous Anne Boleyn and Anne
of Cleves, unkindly described
by Henry as 'the Flanders mare',
Alison Weir shows great insights
into a society and a court where
private emotions and needs
often took precedence over
affairs of state.

Weir, Alison
Children of England
Pimlico pbk £8.99
0712673199
Alison Weir writes popular history at its very best. This book
begins at the point one of her
previous bestsellers, The Six
Wives of Henry VIII, finishes -
the death of Henry. Henry was
survived by three of his children
- Edward, Mary and Elizabeth.
Next in the line of succession
were the descendants of Henry's
sister - also Mary - who included
Lady Jane Grey, Henry's great-
niece, later to be queen for nine
days. Weir's highly readable
account of the characters and
relationships of Henry's four
heirs is set against the background of one of the most turbulent periods in English history
when each of them was potentially the pawn of powerful political and religious figures.

Reproduced from *The Oxford Illustrated History of Tudor and Stuart Britain* (Oxford).

The Stuart Age

Ashley, Maurice
The English Civil War
Sutton pbk £9.99
0750900199

The Illustrated History Paperback series, which includes this title, is an engaging, wide-ranging and readable collection of books aimed at both the student and the general reader. Maurice Ashley's concise and clear analysis of the often confused and perplexing course of events between 1640 and 1651 can be highly recommended as an introduction to its subject, and draws effectively upon contemporary evidence and documentation to throw new light on the political and social conditions of the period.

Aylmer, G.E.
Rebellion or Revolution?
Oxford UP pbk £7.99
0192892126

Those who lived through the events of 1640 to 1660 - civil war, regicide, republic, restoration of the monarchy - were divided on the nature and significance of what they had witnessed. Just as contemporaries were divided in their interpretation of events, so too have historians been ever since. Gerald Aylmer's book serves as both a short history of mid-seventeenth century England and as a survey of current readings of that history.

His own argument that, in so far as there was a revolution it was on the side of the middle class and the Puritans, is powerfully made and he charts both the successes of that revolution and the failures which allowed the traditional ruling classes to regain control.

Carlton, Charles
Charles I: The Personal Monarch
Routledge pbk £14.99
0415125650

This is a book that many reviewers have hailed as the best modern biography of Charles, an insecure and troubled man, unsuited to the role of king, particularly at a time of social and political upheaval. Carlton's achievement is to draw a thoughtful and subtle portrait of the man which goes a long way towards making sense of royal actions and policies which have often seemed perverse and inexplicable. His book is a gripping and ultimately moving account of Charles' life and death.

Carlton, Charles
Going to the Wars
Routledge pbk £15.99
0415103916

What was the experience of fighting in the English Civil War like for the ordinary soldier?

Much has been written on the Civil War - its causes, its campaigns and its battles - but few books have considered this fundamental question. Carlton makes use of a wide variety of sources in order to convey some sense of how the civil war seemed to the men who fought in it - how far, if at all, they understood the wider contexts of the battles in which they took part, how they prepared for the devastating experience of combat and how they dealt with defeat.

Fraser, Antonia
Cromwell: Our Chief of Men
Mandarin pbk £12.99
0749301074

Born into a minor gentry family in Huntingdon, propelled by his own military genius and by the upheavals of the age into a position as the most powerful man in the nation, the trajectory of Cromwell's career was an extraordinary one and his life and character were the subjects of fiery debate by his contemporaries. They have continued to excite controversy since his death in 1658. Antonia Fraser's book is a bold attempt to look beyond the stereotypes and the distortions of royalist propaganda and to create a scrupulously fair biography, suited to the general reader.

Fraser, Antonia
The Gunpowder Plot
Weidenfeld hbk £20.00
029781348
Antonia Fraser is deservedly well known for her skill as a narrative historian and this book is the most recent example of this skill. Turning her attention to one of the most celebrated yet mysterious episodes in English history - the plot by Robert Catesby and his fellow conspirators to blow up Parliament - she has fashioned a gripping story, which convincingly recreates the events leading to the night of 5th November 1605, and provides a credible account of the motivation of Catesby, Guy Fawkes and the other plotters. She steers the reader through the controversies that have raged over the extent to which the plot was a government fabrication designed to discredit Catholics and deftly untangles the complicated relationship between politics and religion which existed in the last years of Elizabeth's reign and the first years of that of James I.

Fraser, Antonia
The Weaker Vessel
Mandarin pbk £8.99
0749316527
Subtitled Women's Lot in Seventeenth Century England, this book is a careful study of the lives and expectations of women in the period. Based on extensive research and written with Antonia Fraser's characteristic verve and skill, The Weaker Vessel brings to life a wide range of individual women, from nuns and governesses to milkmaids and courtesans, and investigates the possibilities that seventeenth century society offered them.

Hibbert, Christopher
Cavaliers and Roundheads
HarperCollins pbk £8.99
0586090088
There have been many single-volume histories of the English Civil War but few as entertaining or as accessible as Hibbert's book. He provides a compelling narrative of the campaigns and battles of the war between King and Parliament, enlivened by astute and revealing character sketches not only of the major participants but also of such lesser but colourful figures as Sir Arthur Aston, the brutal Governor of Oxford, who was beaten to death with his own wooden leg, and Abigail Penington, London's Lady Mayoress, who marched out with other City wives and the fishwives of Billingsgate to work on the capital's foundations.

Hill, Christopher
The English Bible and the Seventeenth Century Revolution
Penguin pbk £9.99
0140159908
The scriptures affected every aspect of society in the England of the seventeenth century. They could be used to justify rebellion against the King and his eventual execution and they could be cited and interpreted in such a way as to call into question every established practice and institution. Equally they could be used to defend the King and his government. Hill's book is a learned but accessible exploration of the ways in which the English Bible had its impact on the lives of individuals and on the wider social, foreign and colonial policies pursued by government.

The Civil War

A small selection of further titles on the English Civil War

There are many one-volume histories of the English Civil War in print and some of these are reviewed in the main text. So too are a small number of more specialised studies of the period. There is, of course, a wealth of other titles available. S.R. Gardiner's seminal work on the subject, **History of the Great Civil War**, first appeared at the end of the nineteenth century but continues to be accepted as the chronological basis for work produced since. Enterprisingly Windrush Press keep the work in print in four volumes. Volume One (0900075104 £9.95) covers the years 1642-44, Volume Two (0900075155 £9.95) the central years of 1644-45, Volume Three (0900075309 £9.95) covers 1645-1647 and the final volume (090007535X £9.95) looks at the last two years, 1647-1649, before the execution of the king. Philip Haythornthwaite's book **The English Civil War: An Illustrated Military History** (Arms and Armour Press 1854093231 £14.99) is a single volume work that focuses exclusively on the military aspects of the war and provides a full account of strategy and tactics in the campaigns. Sutton publish two books which look at the war from a slightly unusual perspective. **The English Civil War Day by Day** (0750909595 £19.99) by Wilfred Emberton is presented in diary form and gathers together knowledge of events in such a way that the reader witnesses events unfolding day by day. Peter Gaunt's **The Cromwellian Gazetteer** (0750900636 £9.99) details all the sites associated with the Parliamentary cause and all the locations throughout Britain and Ireland which still bear evidence of Civil War associations.

Sutton also publish a sequence of books on the Civil War in particular parts of the country, including **The Civil War in Oxfordshire** (0750906006 £12.99) by David Eddershaw, **Gloucester and the Civil War** (0750901489 £12.99) by Malcolm Atkin and Wayne Laughlin and **The Civil War in the Midlands 1642 - 1651** (0750901675 £12.99) by Roy Sherwood which examines the impact of the war on the region that suffered more than any other, and for a longer period of time, from the depredations of the soldiers of both sides. **London and the Civil War** (Macmillan 0333657543 £14.99), edited by Stephen Porter, is a collection of essays which examine the reasons for the capital's allegiance to the parliamentary cause and the effects the war had on London. **Edgehill 1642** (Windrush Press 0900075341 £15.99) by Peter Young is a reprint of a classic account of a particular battle in which the author looks in detail at how a battle was fought in the Civil War.

Much debate over the years has centred on the reasons why civil war became unavoidable. Two books specifically on the subject are readily available. In the series British History in Perspective, **The Causes of the English Civil War** (Macmillan 0333426614 £9.99) by Ann Hughes is a review of recent discussions of the relationship between political and religious controversies in which Hughes emphasises the deep-rooted ideological divisions that existed. **The Causes of the English Civil War** (Oxford UP 019822141X £11.99) by Conrad Russell consists of a series of lectures delivered at Oxford in which the distinguished scholar of the period considers the reasons behind the outbreak of hostilities. Another very distinguished scholar of the seventeenth century is Christopher Hill and **Intellectual Origins of the English Revolution - Revisited** (Oxford UP 0198206682 £20.00) is a revised edition of a major work in which he examines the intellectual forces which prepared minds for the revolution of the 1640s.

Both Russell and Hill have written widely on the seventeenth century and books by them are reviewed on pages 32 and 37. Others of their titles which are readily available include Russell's **The Fall of the British Monarchies** (Oxford UP 0198205880 £14.95), a history of events in the years 1637-1642 in which Charles I's authority in his three kingdoms collapsed, and Hill's **Puritanism and Revolution** (Secker 0436203200 £14.99), a varied collection of essays on the subject of the Puritan Revolution in its broadest definition. Another scholar who has written widely and accessibly on the Civil War years is John Morrill, one of whose books is reviewed on page 36. Other titles include **The Nature of the English Revolution** (Longman 0582089425 £16.99), a collection of essays illustrating the main scholarly debates over the origins, nature and consequences of the revolution, and **Reactions to the English Civil War** (Macmillan 0333275667 £13.50), a volume of essays by different hands in the Problems in Focus series.

Finally, the Civil War is remembered as much for the personalities of those involved in it as for its battles and campaigns. Chief amongst these are, of course, Charles I and Cromwell and books on both of them are reviewed in the section on Stuart England. On Cromwell, Barry Coward's **Oliver Cromwell** (Longman 0582553857 £10.99) is a brief but cogent account of his career, one of a series called Profiles in Power, and **Oliver Cromwell** by Peter Gaunt (Blackwell 0631183574 £6.99) is a recent, concise re-examination of his extraordinary life. Other works on Charles worth examining include the volume in the British History in Perspective series, **Charles I** (Macmillan 033360136X £10.99) by Michael Young, which guides students through the published material on Charles's reign and Kevin Sharpe's **The Personal Rule of Charles I** (Yale UP 0300065965 £16.95) which is a massive and highly-acclaimed analysis of the personality, principles and policies of Charles and an account of his attempts to rule without parliament, attempts which led eventually to the unavoidable conflict known as the Civil War.

Hill, Christopher
God's Englishman
Penguin pbk £8.99
0140137114

Christopher Hill has long been one of the leading authorities on 17th century England. Steeped in the literature of every aspect of the period, he writes with authority and all his work offers illuminating and fascinating insights. His biography of Cromwell was first published some time ago but it remains a compelling interpretation of the life of a man who exerted an extraordinary influence over the course of English history.

Hill, Christopher
The World Turned Upside Down
Penguin pbk £9.99
0140137327

In *The World Turned Upside Down* Christopher Hill draws on his massive reading and his wide-ranging knowledge of the period to produce a fascinating and important study, not of the bourgeois revolution that was (at least temporarily) successful, but of the myriad groups and sects - the Ranters, the Levellers, the Fifth Monarchists - who were demanding a more fundamental overturning of society. Hill's book undertakes the generous task of rescuing these groups and their ideas from what E.P. Thompson, in another context, called 'the enormous condescension of posterity' and, in doing so, redraws the map of seventeenth century social, religious and intellectual history.

Hutton, Ronald
The Rise and Fall of Merry England
Oxford UP pbk £8.99
0192853279

Hutton's highly acclaimed study of the religious and secular rituals which marked the passage of the year in late medieval and early modern England is a fascinating and informative account of May revels and midsummer marching watches, of mummers and Boy Bishops, hobby horses and Lords of Misrule. He carefully explains how traditions developed and were modified in response to wider changes in religion and society and examines the cofrontations that occurred between the supporters of Merry England and the new forces of Puritanism.

Kenyon, John
The Civil Wars of England
Phoenix pbk £9.99
1857994523

Many military historians have analysed the campaigns of the English Civil Wars and have placed the battle plans and strategies of the generals under close scrutiny. Other historians have treated the wars as crucial episodes in the constitutional history of England, seeing the actual fighting as a backdrop to the working out of major political and religious issues. John Kenyon, a leading authority on the Stuart period, has attempted to synthesise both political and military history to produce a concise and telling summation of the wars. Skilful in its narrative and enlivened by trenchant portraits of the leading figures of the times, this is an ideal introduction for the general reader.

Kishlansky, Mark
A Monarchy Transformed : Britain 1603 -1714
Penguin Hbk £25.00
0713990686

The Penguin History of Britain is a major new series, launched in 1996 with two titles, of which this volume is one. As the advisory editor David Cannadine says, 'The close of the twentieth century is an appropriate and challenging time to reassess and rediscover the British past.' Kishlansky's contribution to the series is a vigorous and readable account of the period between the accession of James I and the death of Queen Anne, years in which the aspirations of sovereigns and subjects came into harsh and often bloody conflict and in which political developments led to the emergence of a Britain no longer isolated on the fringes of Europe, but one of the greatest powers of the Western world.

Morrill, John
Cromwell and the English Revolution
Longman pbk £14.99
0582016754

Cromwell is one of the best-known figures in English history but he is also one who has aroused much controversy and has been very variously assessed, both by his contemporaries and by historians in the three centuries since his death. Was he an admirable champion of religious liberty or was he a bigot intent upon the forcible imposition of his own views on others? Was he a successful military figure thrust, somewhat unwillingly, into a political role by the force of events or was he a military dictator interested largely in the consolidation and increase of his own power? Morrill and eight other leading historians of the period consider the debates surrounding Cromwell's career in a work that is of interest to the scholar and the general reader with a particular interest in the period.

Morrill, John (ed)
The Oxford Illustrated History of Tudor and Stuart Britain
Oxford UP Hbk £25.00
019820325X

The two centuries which saw the Reformation take its peculiarly English form, which witnessed civil wars that resulted in the beheading of Charles I and a Glorious Revolution that sent another king into ignominious exile were amongst the most dramatic in the country's history. As well as the political and religious turmoil, demographic changes and the increase in literacy, economic expansion and the shifts in political power and participation wrought far-reaching transformations at all levels of society. John Morrill has edited a volume for the general reader in which eighteen scholars, including such well-known historians as John Guy, Christopher Haigh and Conrad Russell, explore many aspects of the political, religious and cultural history of the period. Authoritative and richly illustrated, this volume is likely to remain a standard introduction to a tumultuous age.

Petegorsky, David
Left-Wing Democracy in the English Civil War
Sutton pbk £14.99
0750910534

The Diggers, led by the pamphleteer and social visionary Gerrard Winstanley, was one of the most radical and imaginative groups that emerged briefly in the world that had been turned upside down by the Civil War. In 1649 and 1650 they established a number of farming communities which attempted to work the land for the benefit of the common people. These experimental communities were short-lived, largely because of the hostility of less radical revolutionaries and of the army, but this century has seen a revival of interest in the Diggers and in Winstanley. This pioneering study of the movement remains one of the best analyses of Winstanley's ideas and provides a challenging interpretation of the political context in which they arose.

Roots, Ivan
The Great Rebellion 1642 - 1660
Sutton pbk £14.99
0750909218

This is a revised edition of a book first published in the sixties and hailed then as 'a masterpiece of compression.' It provides a stimulating account of the origins of the English Civil War, details the course of events in the struggle between King and Parliament and places particular emphasis on the 1650s, a period too often seen, tendentiously, as a mere obstacle to an inevitable Restoration settlement in 1660. Roots's interest is primarily in the political and constitutional but his use of the views of those involved in the events, as well as the diverse interpretations put upon them by historians, is such that he reveals the importance of the interactions of individuals - and the intervention of sheer chance - in shaping larger developments.

Russell, Conrad
Crisis of Parliaments
Oxford UP pbk £14.95
0199130345

The relationship between the monarchy and Parliament dominated much of the politics of the Tudor and Stuart periods and Russell's book is an authoritative study of this relationship. Political, social and economic factors are all considered in the book which returns again and again to the twin themes of the political and constitutional effects of economic fluctuations, particularly rapid inflation, and the difficulties engendered by religious discord in a theologically divided nation.

Smith, A. G. R.
The Emergence of a Nation State
Longman pbk £18.99
0582489741

One of a series entitled Foundations of Modern Britain, Alan Smith's book is a study of the period between the Reformation and the Restoration, a period of upheaval and, often, uncertainty which began with a religious and political crisis and concluded with the return of Charles II, after the years of civil war, the execution of his father and the failed experiment with a republic. It was also the period in which the country was forged into something recognisable as a 'nation state' and in which the acquisition of the first small colonies abroad rehearsed the great expansion of empire which occurred in the following two centuries. Aimed primarily at students and teachers, the book is nonetheless an accessible account for the general reader of the achievements of the Elizabethan and Jacobean periods and the political and social tensions which underlay them.

Somerset, Anne
Unnatural Murder
Weidenfeld hbk £20.00
0297813102

Sir Thomas Overbury was a minor figure in the political and literary worlds of Jacobean England. In 1613, during a period of unwilling lodgement in the Tower of London, he died. Two years later Frances Howard, Countess of Somerset, a renowned beauty at James I's court, and her husband, the Earl of Somerset, a favourite of the ambiguously-sexed James and one of the most powerful men in the kingdom, were put on trial, charged with Overbury's murder. Both were found guilty and sentenced to hang but the king freed them both after short periods of imprisonment. A number of alleged accomplices were less lucky. Around this case Anne Somerset has built a vivid narrative of the lives of those involved and a powerful portrait of the intrigue and scandal of the Jacobean court.

Unnatural Murder :
Poison at the Court of James I

Anne Somerset

The author of a recent best-selling book on the subject describes a Jacobean cause célèbre

In his lifetime Sir Thomas Overbury was an arrogant and unpopular figure whose career at the Jacobean court was a failure. Nevertheless, his mysterious demise in the Tower of London plunged the nation into turmoil. In 1615 it prompted a murder enquiry which culminated in the sentencing to death of Overbury's former best friend, Robert Carr, Earl of Somerset. It was an outcome which shook the country to its foundations, for Somerset was not only a Privy Councillor but occupied the prestigious post of Lord Chamberlain to the King. More shocking still he had risen to prominence as a royal favourite or, in modern parlance, as King James I's boyfriend.

James I was a married man but, despite the fact that in seventeenth century England sodomy was a capital offence, he was apt to become infatuated with handsome male courtiers. In 1607 a young Scot named Robert Carr had become James's 'especially graced man.' Over the next six years the King had showered him with wealth and affection, in return, presumably, for sexual favours. Carr had shared his material gains with his great friend Sir Thomas Overbury, who managed his finances and provided him with political guidance. However, in 1613 the pair quarrelled after Carr determined to marry his twenty-three-year-old mistress, Frances, Countess of Essex.

The Countess of Essex was one of the most beautiful women in the kingdom. Having been unhappily married since her early teens, she longed to separate from her husband in order to wed the royal favourite. In the spring of 1613, this goal seemed attainable, for the King permitted her to petition for an annulment of her marriage on the grounds that witchcraft had rendered the Earl of Essex incapable of consummating their union.

Sir Thomas Overbury detested the Countess of Essex's entire family and regarded Frances as little better than a whore. Determined that she should never become the wife of Robert Carr, he sought to obstruct her annulment. It seems that he threatened to reveal that she and Carr had committed adultery, thus exposing as a lie Frances's claim that she was still a virgin. This prompted the King to intervene: in April 1613 Overbury was imprisoned in the Tower of London on a spurious charge of 'contempt' towards the monarch.

Over the next five months Overbury's health steadily deteriorated, as a result - so it was later claimed - of eating poisoned tarts and jellies sent to him by Lady Essex. In September the sick man sought to improve his health by having an enema, whereupon an apothecary's boy was allegedly bribed to administer poison anally, causing death within twenty-four hours.

Whether or not this was what really killed Overbury cannot be stated for certain. Though poison remains the most likely explanation, it is conceivable that Overbury died from natural causes, or that the medical treatment he received seriously harmed him. Certainly those who conducted the murder investigation, two years later, were concerned less to establish the truth than to procure Somerset's downfall.

Ten days after Overbury died, the Countess of Essex's marriage was annulled. She had earlier been pronounced 'a virgin uncorrupted' by a committee of court ladies who had carried out a gynaecological examination but, though this seemingly vindicated Frances, the finding was received with open derision in many quarters. Three months after her first marriage had been dissolved Frances married Robert Carr, whom the King had now created Earl of Somerset.

For two years the couple lived happily but, when the King became besotted by another exquisite young man, Somerset became vulnerable to the machinations of his enemies. Allegations that Overbury had been poisoned were unearthed, leading to the arrest of the Somersets and several other humbler individuals.

In the autumn of 1615 four of the Somersets' accomplices were brought to trial. At these hearings public outrage was magnified by salacious evidence which was put forward to brand the Countess as a 'lewd and malicious woman'. The prosecution provided details of her adulterous trysts with Somerset, alleging that, when not purchasing poisons, she had resorted to necromancers and used supernatural enchantments to keep her lover enamoured

Despite protesting their innocence, the Somersets' lowborn confederates were found guilty and hanged for their part in Overbury's murder. The Somersets themselves were tried on consecutive days in May 1616. At her arraignment, the Countess pleaded guilty, and the mandatory sentence of death was pronounced on her. The Earl, in contrast, vigorously maintained his innocence, but he defended himself poorly and he too was convicted. Nevertheless, the death sentences imposed on him and his wife were never enacted. After a short period of imprisonment, the Somersets were permitted by the King to retire to the country, lenient treatment that provoked widespread fury.

The impact of the Overbury murder case was enormous. The very fact that poison was involved inspired the utmost horror and revulsion, for Englishmen considered that poisoning was a crime only foreigners would commit, a species of depravity alien to the national character. Furthermore, the reputation of the King was indelibly tarnished. Although James's own role in the arrest and detention of Overbury was glossed over (and still less was there mention of the King's homosexual tendencies), by sparing the Somersets James drew on himself a share of the odium that would otherwise have been reserved for Overbury's murderers. Moralists had long claimed that the court of James I was a fundamentally rotten institution, riddled with sexual vice and other forms of wickedness. The murder of Sir Thomas Overbury provided graphic confirmation of this and was perceived as an extreme manifestation of the corruption and dishonesty that pervaded the court at this period.

Stone, Lawrence
Road to Divorce
Oxford UP pbk £9.99
0192853074

Stone's books are always very well constructed, meticulously researched and crisply written. Using as the basis for *Road to Divorce* the notion that a society's attitude towards the breakdown of marriage is a powerful indicator of moral and cultural values, Stone proceeds to explore the many, and fascinating, ways in which men, women and the legal profession have attempted to deal with the issue of divorce. Using unpublished legal records from 1660 to 1860, this book is a frank, and remarkably intimate look at the personal testimonies of individuals embroiled in the process of disentangling themselves from marital collapse, and offers a clear window onto the huge swings in morality witnessed from 1530 onwards. Stone also develops his own historical analysis in an attempt to explain the rapid increase in divorce from 1920 onwards. Stone's reputation as one of our greatest historians of family life is richly deserved - read his book for the changing rights and status of women alone, and be both illuminated by the author's analysis, and surprised at the historical detail he unearths.

Stone, Lawrence
Family, Sex and Marriage in England 1500 -1800
Penguin pbk £8.99
0140137211

Stone's book offers an authoritative survey of views which came to transform the notion of the family unit. To contemporary eyes, the family of 1500, based as it was on economic security, seems quite alien - pragmatic, cool headed and not at all romantic. Stone takes us through the next three centuries with their increasing emphasis on the needs and wishes of the individual, to 1800 and the much smaller, emotionally tied family unit. The changing state of the family inevitably affected not just the whole idea of marriage and sexuality, but contributed to permanent alterations in areas like education, and threw up major philosophical debates on, for example, the whole issue of contraception. The book offers a wealth of factual evidence which reflects powerfully on notions of family life, both in the period Stone covers and in the present and which overthrows many illusions that people harbour about our domestic past. As Stone himself cheerily comments of the family; '...there is as little reason to have any more confidence in its survival and spread in the future as there is in that of democracy itself.'

Thomas, Keith
Religion and the Decline of Magic
Penguin pbk £14.00
0140137440

The distinctions between religion and magic in 16th and 17th century England were often slight. Both developed to meet the needs of a precarious existence. The majority of the population were uneducated and illiterate. Ignorant of the Scriptures, their faith was grounded in superstition and belief in the magical properties of the Holy Sacraments. The hold of the Church was never so complete as to prevent allegiance to rival forms of belief. Alongside the priests came a redoubtable cast of cunning men, wise women, astrologers, alchemists, geomancers, ghosts, fairies and changelings. Keith Thomas marshals a formidable range of material to provide a clear and enthralling analysis of the subject. He also charts the intellectual and technological changes of the late 17th century which gradually led to the demise of such beliefs.

Underdown, David
Revel, Riot and Rebellion
Oxford UP pbk £8.99
0192851934

What have maypoles and charivari processions to do with the English Civil War? In this original study in seventeenth century social history, David Underdown highlights the links between cultural and political phenomena by showing how strikingly local differences in popular allegiance in the Civil War coincided with regional contrasts in the traditional festive culture. The book provides a novel and intriguing perspective on the Civil War and, in great detail, reveals the everyday behaviour and beliefs of ordinary people in the seventeenth century.

Reproduced from *The Oxford Illustrated History of Tudor and Stuart Britain (Oxford)*.

Wedgwood, C. V.
The King's Peace
Penguin pbk £8.99
0140171576

The King's War
Penguin pbk £8.99
0140171584

These two volumes were first published in the fifties and remain a superb account of some of the most troubled years in British history. The first book is a narrative of the four years of Charles I's reign which immediately preceded the outbreak of the Civil War. It conveys the momentum of events, often bewildering to contemporaries, as the King's Peace was overtaken by the gathering willingness of some of his subjects to resist, violently if necessary, his governance. The second volume details the events of the ensuing war, from Charles's attempted arrest of the Five Members, through the rise of Cromwell and the battles at Marston Moor and Naseby, to the Scots' decision to surrender Charles to the English Parliament. When these books were first published one reviewer wrote what continues to be true forty years later. 'This is history on the grand scale, designed for the enlightenment of the layman and at the same time as a lasting contribution to historical knowledge.'

Wedgwood, C. V.
The Trial of Charles I
Penguin pbk £8.99
0140171592

The final volume in Dame Veronica Wedgwood's sequence of books about the Civil Wars is this brief but telling account of the ten-week period in which Cromwell and his colleagues assumed control of the country, defeated the opposition of both Presbyterians and the radical groups such as the Levellers, silenced their opponents in the Houses of Parliament, brought Charles I to trial and had him executed and a republic declared. The king's execution was felt by contemporaries, even those who urged it as unavoidable, as a peculiarly horrifying event and Wedgwood conveys the full drama of those weeks.

Restoration and Eighteenth Century

Brewer, John
The Pleasures of the Imagination
HarperCollins hbk £30.00
0002555379

The aim of Brewer's book is simply stated. As he writes, 'In 1660, when Charles II was restored to the throne, there were few professional authors, musicians and painters, no public concert series, galleries, newspaper critics or reviews. By the dawn of the nineteenth century they were part of the cultural life of the nation. This book explains how this happened.' In the pursuit of his aim and in his examination of the birth and development of British 'high culture', Brewer presents the reader with a detailed and vivid panorama of the artistic and social activity of the eighteenth century. The growth of publishing and bookselling and the emergence of circulating libraries, the debate between professional painters and gentlemen connoisseurs, the fluctuating fortunes of the theatres and Garrick's strategies for raising the public standing of plays and their performers, the flourishing of the arts in small provincial cities like Chichester and Lichfield - all these subjects, and many others, Brewer illuminates with material drawn from a multitude of published and unpublished sources. He also makes telling use of the many images reproduced in the book, by artists as different as Reynolds and Rowlandson, to elucidate his arguments.

Colley, Linda
Britons
Vintage £8.99
0099427214

Although the politics and social history of the eighteenth century have been relatively neglected as subjects for detailed historical study, Linda Colley argues, in this wide-ranging exploration of the period from the 1707 Act of Union to Catholic Emancipation in 1829, that this was the time in which a new British nation was invented and a new national identity forged. Colley demonstrates convincingly how war, religion, trade and imperial expansion all played a part in the creation of this new sense of identity and also how much of this identity was defined in terms of opposition to prevailing forces in Europe. Britain was protestant, Europe was predominantly Catholic; Britain was a stronghold of representative government, Europe was largely ruled by autocrats. The consequences of that definition by opposition are with us still.

Deane, Phyllis
The First Industrial Revolution
Cambridge UP pbk £12.95
0521296099

The rapid development of the economy that occurred in Britain in the second half of the eighteenth century and first half of the nineteenth century transformed the country into the most powerful industrial nation in the world but brought in its wake dramatic changes in the way most people led their lives and the environments in which they did so. Phyllis Deane's book has long been a standard analysis for students of the huge economic, industrial and technological changes that took place between 1750 and 1850.

Gatrell, V.A.C.
The Hanging Tree
Oxford UP pbk £10.99
0192853325

In the eighteenth century an increasing number of petty crimes became liable to capital punishment and the sixty years between 1770 and 1830 were those in which the bloody reign of Tyburn and other hanging trees claimed its largest number of victims. Some 7000 men and women were executed in the period and their executions

History meets culture

John Brewer

The author of *The Pleasures of the Imagination* reflects the way historians can usefully approach the work of the great artists of the past

Writing the history of works of art and literature, of what is often referred to as 'high culture', is a delicate business. The plays, poems and novels of Shakespeare, Milton, Blake and Austen, the paintings of Holbein, Turner and Constable have been given a special status that takes them out of history and into a timeless realm which makes them not just artefacts of their age but sacred national treasures, conserved in standard editions, or displayed in museums and art galleries. The critic, analysing works of art, explains their impact and effect on our emotions adding to their aura, but the danger for the historian is that by treating a work of art as something that has to be explained rather than worshipped he can be accused of desecration, of belittling what is great by putting it back into its time and place. It's not surprising then, that with a few notable exceptions like Simon Schama, Peter Burke and John Hale, historians have left the history of culture to art and literary critics and to musicologists.

But at the same time history has become fashionable in studies of the arts and literature. Shakespeare scholars study the Bard's changing reputation rather than examining the minutiae of his plays (Gary Taylor's Reinventing Shakespeare: A Cultural History from Restoration to the Present (New York and Oxford: Oxford University Press, 1989) is the most wide-ranging and controversial of several such studies); art historians writing about landscape are as busy reading the agricultural writings of Arthur Young as examining the works of Constable, Cozens or Moreland; studies of Handel by music historians focus on his audiences as much as on the works themselves. This growing concern for history can also be seen in the public presentation of the arts. Most permanent art collections arrange great masters in national schools in a way first developed in the late eighteenth century, but the re-hanging of the National Portrait Gallery and, more surprisingly in a bastion of modernism, the rotating hang at the Tate which exposes the whole collection and not just a select body of masterpieces to public view, put history on a par with aesthetics. At the same time, more and more temporary exhibitions (I'm thinking for instance of a series of brilliant catalogues and shows mounted by Andrew Moore at the Norwich Castle Museum) look at the history of taste and collecting rather than showing off 'great art'. Similarly, though there is a powerful move to mount radical modern interpretations of classical music (like Peter Jonas's sensational version of Handel's Guilio Cesare in Egitto currently playing to packed houses in Munich), the early music movement, attempting to recreate performances in the manner of the seventeenth and eighteenth centuries and with original instruments, depends on careful historical research for it performances.

These developments represent three trends. First, there is a growing interest in the reception of works of art and literature as well as in their creation, in the life of an art-work after its conception. Thus the study of the novel is becoming a history not just of the works of Defoe, Richardson, Austen, Dickens, and Conrad but of novel reading and novel readers. Secondly, canonical works, familiar to us from public museums and school books, have been re-evaluated by studying the circumstances in which they produced, a context which includes the institutions and economy of culture as well as forgotten, minor works. Finally, critics have begun to ask about processes by which our literary and cultural heritage have been formed, asking what forces shaped its values and traditions. Culture is not just made by writers, painters and performers, but also by impresarios and middlemen, and by the public made up of readers, spectators and listeners.

When I was writing The Pleasures of the Imagination, a history of 'high culture' in eighteenth-century England which covers writing, publishing and reading, the visual arts, music and theatre, I was struck by how little historians had contributed to these subjects. It was as if they thought that politics, the economy, and society were the serious matter of history, while high culture was a pleasant diversion - the icing on the cake - which was best left to others of a more aesthetic disposition. This seems to me an error on two counts. As art historians and literary critics have shown, high culture is never separate or above a nation's politics, economy and society, but an essential part of it; moreover, historians' archival skills make them especially well placed to show this. Of course, as I discovered in writing The Pleasures of the Imagination, such an approach made people uneasy. Editors in publishing houses were worried that in uncovering the financial deals and personal intrigues of artists and impresarios, in writing about the changing reputation and self-promoting efforts of major literary and artistic figures, and in treating culture not as a collection of fondly remembered great works, but as made up of conflicts and quarrels, vested interests and a constant (often unsuccessful) struggle for respectability, I would demean the artist and works they admired and cherished. But this is a nonsense. There is always more than one way to look at works of art; always more than one story that can be told. And historians can show that it is valuable to view high culture not just as an inert monument to an earlier age but as what was once (and will continue to be) a dynamic force which shapes society and moulds its values.

provided a grisly public theatre for many thousands more. Gatrell's massive and scholarly work explores, in fascinating detail, the responses of English men and women of all classes to the brutal spectacles witnessed on the scaffold. He draws skilfully on a wide variety of sources - letters, literary works, ballads and broadsheets - to illuminate the period's attitudes and reactions to public execution.

Langford, Paul
A Polite and Commercial People
Oxford UP pbk £10.95
0192852531
This was the first volume to appear in the New Oxford History of England and offers the reader a comprehensive and up-to-date overview of the period between the accession of George II and the loss of the American colonies.

Interspersing chapters of narrative, which provide an account of both home and foreign affairs, with themed chapters which cover subjects as diverse as the development of spas and the rise of Methodism, the Gothic revival and the prevalence of duelling, Langford skilfully marshals a vast array of evidence to provide a coherent picture of eighteenth century England.

Linebaugh, Peter
The London Hanged
Penguin pbk £9.99
0140132627
The gallows at Tyburn was part of the ordinary social landscape of eighteenth century London. Linebaugh's bold and sweeping book examines how it played an exemplary role in protecting private property and looks at the relationship between crime and Georgian London's working class. His painstaking research reveals the conditions of life amongst those whom the burgeoning consumer society consumed and forms the basis for rich speculation on the economic and social history of the period.

Mathias, Peter
The First Industrial Nation
Routledge £12.95
041502756X
A standard textbook on British economic history between 1700 and 1914, for both A Level students and undergraduates, Mathias' work explains clearly the process of development which led Britain into becoming the first and, for much of the period under examination, the

greatest industrial power in the world. He also throws light on the difficulties brought about by the pressures of industrialisation and studies the relationship between the various sectors in the burgeoning economy.

Porter, Roy
English Society in the Eighteenth Century
Penguin pbk £7.99
0140138196
This volume in the Penguin Social History of Britain is the second edition of a work first published in 1982. With his characteristic wit and fluency, Porter has drawn on a wide variety of evidence to paint a portrait of a nation with a stable though flexible political order, a developing economy and a rich and expanding culture. Ballads and pamphlets, paintings and plays, rural life and metropolitan life, work and leisure - all these subjects and many more are covered by this survey of the social history of the eighteenth century.

Thompson, E. P.
Customs in Common
Penguin pbk £11.00
0140125566

Thompson's analysis of eighteenth century plebeian culture and tradition reveals the way in which the lower classes regulated their lives without recourse to the laws and institutions of the gentry. Amongst the social phenomena he examines are 'wife sales' as a means of divorce, 'rough music' as a system of folk justice and the role of rioting in plebeian resistance to exploitation. His lively account shows just how folklore could be seen as an alternative to the law and how class would dictate the system of beliefs by which a person would structure his or her social experience.

Tillyard, Stella
Aristocrats
Vintage pbk £8.99
0099477114

Aristocrats is the story of four sisters - Caroline, Emily, Louisa and Sarah Lennox - whose lives span the period from 1740 - 1832. Drawing on the rich source of the many letters written by and to the sisters, descendants of Charles II who lived at the heart of the English and Irish aristocracies, Tillyard creates an original portrait of Georgian political and private life. The book moves from personal details - the fashions and books they enjoyed, the marriages, elopements and entanglements of a large family - to the broader perspectives of eighteenth century politics, rebellion in Ireland and revolution in France in an elegant and readable narrative.

Tillyard, Stella
Citizen Lord
Chatto hbk £15.99
0701165383

The younger son of the Duke of Leinster and a cousin of Charles James Fox, Lord Edward Fitzgerald (1763 - 1798) was excited by the revolutionary ideas of the period in which he grew up and joined the militantly anti-English United Irishmen in 1796. He rose rapidly in its hierarchy and, because of his earlier experience in the British army, became its military commander. Fitzgerald was badly wounded in a pre-emptive strike by the authorities against the planned Irish Rebellion of 1798 and died in prison, thus elevating himself to a position in the pantheon of Irish martyr-patriots. Stella Tillyard's book tells the story of Fitzgerald's dramatic life through the use of his letters and those of his family.

Walvin, James
Black Ivory
HarperCollins pbk £8.99
0006862926

This history of black slavery in the British colonies of the West Indies and pre-1776 America seeks to be not a chronological account but an exploration of the major experiences - the brutal conditions on the slave ships, plantation life in the slave colonies, the struggle to maintain dignity - which bound together the men, women and children from diverse African backgrounds who were scattered throughout these colonies. Walvin's sense of narrative, his wide scholarly reading and his readable prose style combine to show how the slave trade, the greatest obscenity perpetrated by Britain, transformed forever the face of America and Africa and provided the morally indefensible stimulus to a huge increase in British maritime power and the wealth it created.

The Cinderella Century

Linda Colley

The author of *Britons* explains why the eighteenth century, so often neglected by older historians, is now the subject of so much exciting work

The eighteenth century has long been something of a Cinderella in British history. Even today, many schools and universities are still inclined to leave it out of their syllabi, leaping from the blood and debate of the civil wars in the 1640s to the iron and coal of the classic Industrial Revolution with scarcely a glance at events in between.

The reasons for this neglect run very deep. In the Victorian and Edwardian eras, eighteenth century Britain was commonly viewed as corrupt and over-mannered, its culture unappreciated. Between the wars, and even after, elegant Georgian squares and terraces were massively demolished in London, Edinburgh, Dublin and many provincial cities, with few voices raised in protest. Eighteenth century British art had few admirers either. As late as the 1950s and 1960s, American collectors in particular were able to snap up wonderful canvases and objects from this period at what seem now unbelievably knock-down prices.

For as long as Britain remained an imperial state, the eighteenth century was also problematic, an embarrassment even, because it witnessed the 'loss' of the American colonies. This century's best-known historian of the period, Lewis Namier (1888-1960) devoted much of his life to illuminating this crisis. But it didn't help much. Namier had a brilliant and highly individualistic mind but his dense and detailed books gave many the impression that eighteenth century British history was labyrinthine, narrow and arid. Just too plain difficult for mass consumption.

Yet over the past two decades or so, much of this has changed. In terms of attracting controversy and broad attention, books on the eighteenth century have been highly successful. Why? Part of the answer is that historians in the field have broadened their vision. E.P. Thompson and his many followers deliberately looked away from the courtly interiors and stately homes that were Namier's hunting ground and focused a sympathetic and enquiring gaze instead on the poor, the criminal, the rebels. The eighteenth century middle class too has found a new wave of chroniclers and admirers.

More dramatically, though, historians are finally coming to terms with the fact that in the eighteenth century the boundaries of Britain dramatically expanded in all sorts of ways. First and obviously this was a period which began with the Act of Union with Scotland (1707) and ended with the Act of Union with Ireland (1800-1). So the challenge of writing a genuinely 'British' history that can do justice to these very different cultures, and to the English and Welsh, without glossing over the real differences between them, is particularly pressing. Secondly, in this period - as in our own - Britain's relationship with Continental Europe was shifting and highly contentious. For most of the eighteenth century, Britain and Ireland were ruled by German kings, the Hanoverians. Indeed, until 1837, the regnal link with the electorate of Hanover gave Britain a territorial stake in the heart of Europe. This was one reason why Britain became involved in an extraordinary succession of major wars with the prime European power of this period, France.

Out of these wars, bloodily, expensively and, as we now know, precariously, emerged an empire which encompassed perhaps a fifth of the world's population by the start of the nineteenth century. Our own post-imperial Britain is perhaps now sufficiently distant from these events to view them with a critical but searchingly curious eye. Certainly I would be prepared to bet a great deal that - just as interest in the British eighteenth century has soared with the willingness to address Wales, Scotland, Ireland and England in tandem, and to locate all of these countries in a broad European context - so, in the future, scores of imaginative scholars are going to be settling profitably and iconoclastically on Britain's global connexions in this period.

Looking at empire broadly will involve far more than that re-hash of battles, treaties and colonial administration which used to be the mainstay of so much traditional imperial history. Historians will have to wrestle (and are beginning to do so) with complex issues of race, ecology, identity, the sheer strangeness of what happened. They will have to study Britain's imperial enterprise in parallel with that of other states, not just the Western European empires of France, Spain and Portugal, but the Russian, Turkish, Chinese empires even. They will have to look hard at the colonised and ask just how far they really were. In short they will have to find ways of bridging British, European and extra-European histories.

So the story of eighteenth century Britain will just keep getting bigger, more controversial, more interdisciplinary. And all this can only be good. Cinderella is having a ball!

Nineteenth Century

Barret-Ducrocq, Francois
Love in the Time of Victoria
Penguin pbk £7.99
0140173269

Barret-Ducrocq ransacks the archives of a London foundling hospital and unearths moving and dramatic evidence of attitudes to sexuality and desire amongst the Victorian working classes. Love letters and other written testimony from working class women discuss love and sex, flirtation and prostitution, promises made and not kept and the terrible burdens of facing pregnancy alone. The author restores dignity and individuality to these women whilst revealing a previously hidden social history.

Bentley, Michael
Politics without Democracy 1815 - 1914
Fontana pbk £8.99
0006863426

'At no time during the period discussed in this book did Britain experience democracy. At no time, equally, were politicians unconscious of its existence as an inspiration, a dismal inevitability or a remote and controllable tendency.'

Thus Bentley describes the period covered by his accessible study of nineteenth century politics and government. His book considers the process by which the major political figures - Peel, Disraeli, Gladstone, Salisbury - took their policy decisions as they and their colleagues strove to control, manipulate and (in many instances) hold back the onset of 'democracy'. In doing so he provides a new perspective on the debates about how Britain moved from a society ruled by a landed oligarchy towards one responsive to the demands of the newly industrialised masses.

Best, Geoffrey
Mid-Victorian Britain
Fontana pbk £6.99
0006860214

For many the Great Exhibition of 1851 was the highpoint of Victorian Society. Professor Geoffrey Best uses this landmark year as a starting point for his quarter of a century study of a society undergoing tremendous changes in an increasingly 'industrial' and 'urban' age. Providing insights into the professional and personal lives

of the citizens of this evolving nation, Professor Best places Mid-Victorian Britain in its social, economic and political context. His traditional approach to historical analysis is often enlivened by quoting from distinguished works of literature of the period. Dickens, Trollope and Wilkie Collins all give what the author terms 'literary evidence' to illustrate prominent aspects of contemporary life for the Mid-Victorians.

Briggs, Asa
Age of Improvement
Longman pbk £17.99
0582491002

Since first publication in 1959, *The Age of Improvement* has sold tens of thousands of copies and has come to be accepted as a classic of modern historical writing, still much used in schools as a textbook, although Briggs's gifts as a writer make it readily accessible to the general reader. His stress on the underlying unities of the age and his analysis of the social problems that came in the wake of startling economic and technological change are particularly valuable.

Briggs, Asa
Victorian Cities
Penguin pbk £8.99
0140135820

Victorian People
Penguin pbk £7.99
0140131337

Victorian Things
Penguin pbk £8.99
0140126775

These three books, published over a period of thirty five years, taken together, constitute an extraordinary and wide-ranging survey of Victorian culture. When the first of them, *Victorian People*, was published in the early fifties, it was one of the indications of changing attitudes to the Victorians, often misunderstood, even caricatured by the generations which succeeded them. By the time Briggs's study of the cities in which the Victorians lived appeared in the sixties, a resurgence of interest in the period was well underway, one to which his work had made a significant contribution. The final volume of the loosely-linked trilogy, *Victorian Things*, was published in 1988 when many of the objects which the Victorians designed and produced, bought and sold, had become valuable collectors' pieces. These three books are all distinguished by their breadth of scholarship and readability and are fundamental texts for anyone wishing to understand the period and its culture.

Cannadine, David
Aspects of Aristocracy
Penguin pbk £7.99
0140249532

Cannadine's collection of inter-connected essays on the British aristocracy in the nineteenth and twentieth centuries represents a concerted effort to reassess the significance of the upper classes in the period. The essays examine both general themes - the extent of aristocratic indebtedness, the degree to which the ranks of the aristocracy were open to the socially mobile - and the careers of individual members of the upper classes, including both well-known figures such as Churchill and Lord Curzon and those such as Lord Strickland and the Cozens-Hardy family who, less familiar to succeeding generations, nonetheless exemplify important strands in Cannadine's multi-faceted argument.

Cannadine, David
The Decline and Fall of the British Aristocracy
Papermac pbk £15.00
0333652185

This is a ground-breaking study of the fading fortunes of the British aristocracy during the last century. Cannadine recounts the process by which notables and nobles have lost much of their wealth, power and prestige and looks closely at the erosion of the traditional system of titles and honours. The result is a compelling account, enlivened by pen portraits of some of the often unusual scions of the aristocracy, of one of the most significant shifts in modern British history.

Chesney, Kellow
The Victorian Underworld
Penguin pbk £8.99
0140139702

Beginning his survey with the tramps, beggars, circus-folk, gypsies and tinkers who inhabited the fringes of society, Chesney proceeds to submerge the reader in the verminous slums of Victorian England. The criminal world he reveals - a world of con-artists, garrotters, pickpockets and prostitutes of all ages that boiled beneath the respectable surface of the nation - was as turbulent and vicious as any since. Chesney's book is a brilliant analysis of the realities behind some of the fictional portrayals of the underbelly of Victorian life, the milieu in which the real Fagin, the real Bill Sikes and the real Nancy moved.

Ensor, R. C. K.
England 1870 - 1914
Oxford UP pbk £10.95
0192852612

Originally published as one of the volumes in the *Oxford History of England,* Ensor's book continues to provide a detailed account of the political and social history of a period of rapid change in English society. From the reforms of Gladstone's first ministry, through the rivalry of Gladstone and Disraeli, the divisive challenges of the Home Rule debate and the Boer War, to the outbreak of World War One, Ensor is a clarifying guide to the complexities of these years.

Evans, Eric
The Forging of the Modern State
Longman pbk £18.99
0582089530

The period covered by this text in the Foundations of Modern Britain series was a period of unprecedented and revolutionary change in the industrial and economic sphere, change which was not mirrored in the political sphere. In 1870, despite the upheavals of the previous century, Britain was still governed largely by a wealthy land-owning class, although one which had learned to adapt its policies and attitudes to new conditions. How change came about and how the landed élite retained their political power are central themes in the book, which also explores the basis of British expansion overseas and the growing demand for political and social reform at home. Intended primarily for students and teachers, the book is organised to meet their practical requirements and concludes with an extensive compendium of factual data.

Fraser, Flora
The Unruly Queen
Papermac pbk £10.00
0333663039

George IV married Caroline of Brunswick in 1795, when he was Prince of Wales. The two were even more disastrously incompatible than some more recent royal couples and they separated the following year, Caroline retreating into exile abroad. However, when George came to the throne in 1820, Caroline decided that she wished to return to England and take her place as Queen. Despite attempts through Parliament to strip her of her title, she was popular with the public and her cause was seized upon by the Whigs and Radicals in opposition. After a farcical scene at George's coronation, when she was denied admission, she continued to maintain her right to be acknowledged but died at Hammersmith a few weeks later. Flora Fraser's book is a lively and readable account of this flamboyant and, perhaps, misunderstood figure.

Golby, J.M
Culture and Society in Britain 1850 - 1890
Oxford UP pbk £9.99
0198711123

Compiled as an Open University Set Text, this is a varied collection of writings from the second half of the nineteenth century. It includes material ranging from Marx to Mrs Beeton, from extracts from novels by George Eliot and poems by Tennyson to letters by Gladstone and diary entries by Kilvert. Although the book was specifically designed for students on a particular Open University course, the choice of documents is sufficiently broad and eclectic to appeal to anyone with an interest in the period.

Harris, Jose
Social History of Britain 1870 - 1914
Penguin pbk £7.99
0140125485

Harris argues strongly, in this volume in the Penguin Social History, that the period he surveys was one in which a clear break with the earlier years of Victorian Britain can be detected. The beliefs that were established in these years, about family and gender, about work and leisure, about religion and the state (and the social structures which embodied these beliefs) continued to dominate British society until the 1960s.

James, Lawrence
The Rise and Fall of the British Empire
Abacus pbk £9.99
0349106673

Lawrence James's examination of the British Imperial experience and its legacy works as an excellent introduction to a subject area which has been much contested in the last thirty years. The chronological narrative and dispassionate tone that the author adopts combine to make a complex and diverse subject accessible without being reductive. Most enlightening of all is the author's dissection of the mental impact that the Empire had on the British themselves. The expansion of three hundred years, followed by rapid decline and retreat, affected a series of changes in the national character: the echoes of these are still present in modern Britain.

Jenkins, Roy
Gladstone
Papermac pbk £10.00
0333662091

Gladstone emerges from the pages of Jenkins' biography as the defining figure of nineteenth century politics, crossing the divide between the rural oligarchy that ruled the nation when he entered politics to the democracy that was emerging in the latter stages of his long career. As such an experienced politician himself, Jenkins is unsurprisingly good at guiding the reader through the intricacies of Gladstone's time in government and in clarifying difficult issues such as the campaign for Home Rule in Ireland, which led to the ruinous division of his party in 1886. His biography, which won the Whitbread biography award, is likely to remain the definitive life of an extraordinary and complex man.

Judd, Denis
Empire
Fontana pbk £9.99
0006379745

The British Empire, the largest the world has ever known, was, famously, the empire upon which the sun never set. However, in the years since the end of the Second World War, the sun *has* set, with dramatic suddennesss, and Britain is still coming to terms with the fact that only a few dots of red remain on the map of the world where, at the height of the empire, more than a quarter of the earth's territory was so coloured. Denis Judd's wide-ranging and accessible survey of the British imperial experience, from 1776 to the present day, pays particular attention to the impact of the empire on both the rulers and the ruled. He examines the major crises of the empire, such as the Indian Mutiny, appraises it in its Victorian heyday and considers its pragmatic transformation into the Commonwealth of today.

Mayhew, Henry
London Labour and the London Poor
Penguin pbk £9.99
0140432418

Mayhew (1812 -1887) was a prolific journalist, playwright and novelist who also co-founded and, briefly, edited *Punch.* He is remembered today for the series of investigative articles he wrote for the *Morning Chronicle* in the late 1840s, in which he laid bare the privations and miseries suffered by the poor in London. Mayhew's journalistic skill, curiosity and compassion combined to produce a succession of graphic portraits of life among the lower classes in the capital, often told in the vividly reported language of those with whom he spoke. His reliability as a reporter has sometimes been questioned but the liveliness and memorability of his bulletins from the lower depths of Victorian London have not.

Reproduced from the *Illustrated History of Europe* (Weidenfeld & Nicolson).

McCord, Norman
British History 1815 -1906
Oxford UP pbk £12.99
0198228589

During the years covered by McCord's book Britain was transformed from a largely rural nation to an industrial one. McCord examines the social, political and economic consequences of this transformation in a work which looks at how such factors as the dramatic increase in the population and the changing nature of the class structure affected the government and administration of the country.

Morris, James
Heaven's Command
Penguin pbk £8.99
0140049266
Pax Britannica
Penguin pbk £8.99
0140049274
Farewell the Trumpets
Penguin pbk £9.99
0140049282

This trilogy, written by a graceful and witty prose stylist, is both a vast panorama of the British

Empire's rise and fall in the Victorian era and beyond and a more intimate study of the lives of the men and women who built it and administered it, 'those astonishing people,' as one critic wrote, 'who, with their bloody-minded benevolence, changed the face of the world.' The first volume covers the sixty years from Victoria's accession to the Diamond Jubilee in 1897, the second book is a wide-ranging portrait of the empire at its apogee in that year and the final volume examines the decline from imperial grandeur in the seventy succeding years up to the nineteen sixties. Morris's easy combination of scholarship with anecdote make all three books a pleasure to read.

Perkin, Harold
Origins of Modern English Society
Routledge pbk £13.99
0415059224

Perkin's bold and original book examines the period of transition known as the Industrial Revolution and argues that it was not merely a sequence of technological changes but a social revolution and a social process from which emerged modern notions of class. Much of what we recognise as characteristic of late twentieth century English society, trends in social and political organisation as well as the achievements of science and technology, is a direct development of forces set in motion in the England of George III and Perkin traces that development with remarkable skill.

Porter, Bernard
The Lion's Share
Longman pbk £15.99
0582089433

This revised third edition of a work often regarded as the best short study of British imperialism in the years since 1850 takes into consideration the wealth of recent scholarship, and the fresh availability of archival material, to provide a vigorous narrative, accessible to the general reader. Porter argues that imperialism was, for Britain at least, more an expression of decline than of strength, masking a serious economic malaise which was established in the late nineteenth century, the legacies of which still haunt us. Too often Britain was controlled by the empire, rather than in control of it, and freedom of action was too often hampered by a need to retain what had been so rapidly, and often so haphazardly, acquired.

Richardson, Ruth
Death, Dissection and the Destitute
Penguin pbk £8.99
0140228624
This remarkable study centres on the 1832 Anatomy Act which, in effect, transformed what had been a feared and hated punishment for murder into one for poverty. Before the act was passed, corpses for dissection by the medical profession were those of convicted murderers (and, notoriously, those unlucky enough to be disinterred by bodysnatchers or despatched by the likes of Burke and Hare). However the Act specified that the bodies should be those of paupers who had died in hospitals and work-houses, too poor to afford a funeral. Richardson's book is simultaneously a compassionate and scholarly account of English attitudes to death over several centuries, a revelation of the often shabby manipulativeness of politicians in passing the Act, and a study of the long aftermath of its passing as reflected in working class fears of the workhouse and a pauper's grave.

Thompson, E. P.
The Making of the English Working Class
Penguin pbk £9.99
0140136037
Arguably the finest and most influential work by a British historian since the war, Thompson's book is a magisterial survey of artisan and working class society in the years between 1780 and 1832. Its great strength lies in the detail of Thompson's research and the power of his historical imagination. He sees the ordinary people of England not as statistical fodder, not as passive victims of the Industrial Revolution but as active participants in shaping their own destinies. In his own words he rescues them from 'the enormous condescension of posterity'.

Thompson, F.M.L.
The Rise of Respectable Society
Fontana pbk £8.99
0006861571
In this reinterpretation of the Victorian period, Thompson maps the social landscape of nineteenth century England through close examination of marriage and the family, work and leisure. The complexities of Victorian class distinctions are revealed, the subtler gradations existing within broad terms like 'working class' or 'middle class', and the extent to which developing notions of self-respect within the classes contributed to Britain's avoidance of the revolutionary upheavals which occurred in other European countries.

Wiener, Martin
English Culture and the Decline of the Industrial Spirit
Penguin pbk £7.50
0140136967
'In the world's first industrial nation, industrialisation did not seem quite at home. In the country that had started mankind on the 'great ascent', economic growth was frequently viewed with suspicion and disdain.' Thus Wiener, in his preface, expresses the paradox that is at the heart of this study of an ambivalence apparent in English culture from the mid-nineteenth century to the present. Hostility to industrialism can be seen in writers like Dickens, Ruskin and Arnold, in the quaint rusticity of the planned garden suburbs of the early twentieth century, in the desire of many nineteenth century businessmen to swop the role of entrepreneur for the more socially rewarding one of English gentleman, and in a host of other cultural manifestations. Wiener maps out this broad range of cultural expressions of a disdain for industrialisation and traces in it the roots of current economic malaise.

Twentieth Century

Addison, Paul
The Road to 1945
Pimlico pbk £10.00
0712659323

In the 1945 general election Labour won a decisive victory, claiming 394 seats and achieving an overall majority of 146. In this book, published in a revised edition, Paul Addison gives a comprehensive account of British politics in the period immediately before, during and immmediately after the Second World War. He traces the shift in political power which enabled Attlee and his colleagues to launch their concerted effort to rebuild British society. Addison is a writer of wit and scholarship and his book was rightly acclaimed by the TLS on first publication as 'a landmark in the writing of contemporary history.'

Barnett, Correlli
The Audit of War
Pan pbk £8.99
033034790X

Correlli Barnett has long been an able proponent of the theory that Britain's decline and fall as a great power has deep roots in the past. This text draws on a wide variety of sources, including unpublished government records, to show that Britain's wartime performance, far from marking a zenith of national achievement, was characterised by all the shortcomings and failures which Barnett has identified in British policy and decision-making over a long period of time.

Barnett, Correlli
The Collapse of British Power
Sutton pbk £10.99
0862990742

'The summer of 1940.. marked the consummation of an astonishing decline in British fortunes....it was a sorry and contemptible plight for a great power, and it derived neither from bad luck, nor from the failures of others. It had been brought down upon the British by themselves.' Thus writes Barnett in the first chapter of what is the fullest explication of his thesis about the decay of British power in this century. He draws upon a wide range of evidence and documentation to support his argument in this controversial and idiosyncratic work.

Barnett, Correlli
Lost Victory
Pan pbk £8.99
0330346393

Barnett is scathing about what he sees as the failings of the Labour government of 1945-50 which, he argues, adopted the short term plan of using the huge American loans, and the money made available in the Marshall Plan, to underwrite the costs of its policies and refused to look at long term plans for modernising Britain. Barnett's thesis is a controversial one but he makes telling use of Cabinet documents and Whitehall records.

Calder, Angus
The Myth of the Blitz
Pimlico pbk £12.50
0712698205

Deeply embedded in popular British notions about the Second World War, amongst both those who lived through it and those who were born later, is the Myth of the Blitz, the idea of a nation smiling through adversity, snatching victory from the jaws of defeat because all classes pulled together and muddled through. This idea of the Blitz emerges, at least in part, from the actual events of 1940-41, but it is also a media-created interpretation which ignores inconveniently contra-dictory facts. More than a quarter of London's population fled to the country. Churchill and the royal family were booed while touring the aftermath of air-raids. Calder's stylish book

Clarke, Peter
Hope and Glory : Britain 1900 - 1990
Penguin Hbk £25.00
0713990716
One of the two volumes so far published in the new Penguin History of Britain, Peter Clarke's book is one that faces up to the challenges of writing the history of a period most of which is still within living memory. His title reveals his fundamental theme. As he writes, 'During the twentieth century Britain still had its moments of glory, not all of them illusory; and Britons nourished hopes, not all of them misguided.'

Dangerfield, George
The Strange Death of Liberal England
Serif pbk £14.99
1897959303
The years before the First World War are often represented as a lost golden age, a glorious Indian summer in which English society basked in its wealth and power before the devastating upheaval of the war. Dangerfield's classic work of popular history demolishes this myth with wit and style, showing how three factors combined to bring Liberal England to its knees - the Home Rule crisis which brought Ireland to the brink of civil war, the campaign for women's suffrage which discredited many of the nation's political and legal institutions, and a wave of industrial unrest which threatened to develop into an all-out General Strike. The frictions and uncertainties of a society that had long

deconstructs the Myth of the Blitz and enhances understanding of a critical period of modern British history.

Calder, Angus
The People's War
Pimlico pbk £15.00
0712652841
'The chief aim of this book', wrote Angus Calder in his foreword, 'is to describe, as accurately as possible, the effect of the war on civilian life in Britain.' In his epic social history of the years from 1939 to 1945, he succeeds superbly in presenting not only the great events and the leading figures but also the textures of everyday life and the parts played by ordinary people in the war effort. Drawing on a wide array of sources, he debunks many of the myths about the war which have survived to the present day but makes clear just how all-encompassing 'total war' proved to be, and how far-reaching it was in its effects on all aspects of British society.

considered itself all-powerful are entertainingly revealed in a book that Eric Hobsbawm has described as 'the most exciting way to start looking at the nation's history during this period.'

Davies, Andrew
To Build a New Jerusalem
Abacus pbk £9.99
0349108099
Subtitled *The British Labour Party from Keir Hardy to Tony Blair*, this book traces the development of the party from its beginnings in the Labour Representation Committee to the present day. Concentrating on individuals and issues, Davies provides lively accounts of the lives and careers of key figures - Ramsay MacDonald, Clement Attlee, Aneurin Bevan, Harold Wilson - and analyses the recurring debates on the economy, on defence and on Europe which have often divided the party. Together with Pelling's more academic study, this book provides the general reader with all he or she needs to know about the People's Party.

Gilbert, Martin
The Day War Ended
Fontana pbk £7.99
0006863442
In May 1945 the war against Germany, begun five and a half years earlier with Hitler's invasion of Poland, came to an end and a dozen European capitals saw a great explosion of joyous celebrations. Allied soldiers celebrated in towns and fields where battles had been fought and civilians rejoiced in cities that had spent years under Nazi occupation. Martin Gilbert has compiled a vividly readable account of what people were thinking and doing on VE Day.

Reproduced from *The Oxford Illustrated Encyclopedia of World History Vol. 2 (Oxford)*.

Hennessy, Peter
Never Again
Vintage pbk £9.99
0099301210
This study of Britain in the years of Attlee's Labour government of 1945 - 51, the first in a projected history of the nation in the second half of the century, won several prizes when it was first published, including the 1993 NCR Award for Non-Fiction. As an academic who spent ten years working as a full-time journalist for the Times and the Financial Times, Hennessy is ideally suited to the writing of contemporary history and his book is a carefully researched and readable account of both the politics and the everyday experience of the period.

Kennedy, Paul
The Realities Behind Diplomacy
Fontana pbk £8.99
0006860044
In the century following the death of Palmerston in 1865, Britain was reduced from the world's leading nation to a country which, in economic and military terms, was less than a second-rate power. Kennedy's analysis of the factors that brought about this decline concentrates on the relationship between Britain's industrial and financial position and its foreign policy, and on the effects of domestic concerns and the rivalries of party politics upon its diplomats and statesmen.

Lee, Stephen
Aspects of British Political History 1914 - 1995
Routledge pbk £12.99
0415131030
Lee is an experienced writer and teacher and this volume is designed to guide A-level students and undergraduates through the major themes and issues of the period. By synthesising the great body of recent research and by examining long-studied topics from fresh perspectives, he produces a book that is clear and digestible and directly relevant to the questions and debates students are likely to confront.

Marwick, Arthur
British Society Since 1945
Penguin pbk £8.99
0140249397
This volume in the Penguin Social History of Britain explores the striking changes and developments in family, race, gender and class relations, in sexual attitudes, in material conditions, in high and popular culture and in technology that have occurred since the end of the war. In the new edition an extensive section on the decade of Thatcher's revolution - the era of privatization and the enterprise culture, of yuppies and football hooliganism - has been added.

Morgan, Kenneth
The People's Peace
Oxford UP pbk £9.99
0192852523

In *The People's Peace* Morgan has written a comprehensive and authoritative history of Britain from the end of the Second World War to the beginning of the nineties. From his chrono-logical narrative - through the period of Attlee's government, the long years of Tory rule in the fifties and early sixties, Wilson's return of Labour to power, the difficult years of the seventies and the first decade of Thatcherism - recurring themes emerge which Morgan analyses with insight and intelligence. Although essentially a political history, this book also, necessarily, engages with the troubles that have haunted the British economy through much of the period he covers, and with the great changes in cultural and social life that have taken place.

Pearce, Malcolm & Stewart, Geoffrey
British Political History 1867 - 1995
Routledge pbk £15.99
0415138124

Two highly experienced teachers have worked together to produce this lively and comprehensive textbook which covers more than a century of British politics from the Second Reform Act to Thatcherism. Each chapter examines the issues within a chosen topic and presents the debates and controversies in historical interpretation of that topic. Much contemporary material - documents, cartoons, extensive quotes - is employed to illuminate the broad themes the book tackles, and every effort is made to set political history within a wider cultural, economic and social context. The book provides an invaluable and wide-ranging introduction to its subject for A-Level students and for undergraduates.

Pelling, Henry
A Short History of the Labour Party
Macmillan pbk £12.95
0333644492

Pelling's book has long been the best available short account of the Labour Party's history since its origins in the trades unions and socialist societies in the late nineteenth century and its formal foundation in 1906. This latest, eleventh, edition was published in 1996 and covers both the choice of Tony Blair to succeed John Smith and the subsequent redrafting of the party's statement of aims in its constitution. Pelling deals con-cisely with the major events in the party's history and provides a useful analysis of recurring issues in the party.

Robbins, Keith
The Eclipse of a Great Power 1870 - 1992
Longman pbk £17.99
0582096111

When this volume of the Foundations of Modern Britain series was first published in 1983, Paul Kennedy wrote that it was 'a concise, balanced account of the past hundred years of British history, and, as such, bids fair to become a standard work.' The revised edition of 1994 added a fifth chronological section to the text, which placed the Thatcher years in historical context, and the book continues to offer students and general readers an overview of the British experience in the period and of the nation's chang-ing role as a former superpower, poised between America and Europe, between an imperial legacy and the uncertainties of the future.

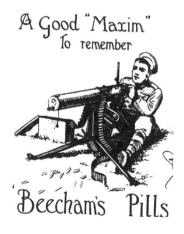

A Good "Maxim" To remember

Beecham's Pills

Roberts, Andrew
Eminent Churchillians
Phoenix pbk £7.99
185799213X

Andrew Roberts is one of the most able and most visible of his generation of historians, a regular political commentator for the Daily Telegraph and Daily Mail as well as the acclaimed biographer of Lord Halifax, foreign secretary at the outbreak of World War II. In this collection of biographical essays, modelled on Strachey's *Eminent Victorians* and written to illuminate various aspects of British history in the period of Churchill's domination of the Conservative Party, he combines original historical analysis with the same irreverent wit that marked Strachey's book. His forceful and opinionated portraits of his chosen subjects - from Lord Mountbatten to the Conservative minister Walter Monckton - are sceptical, often caustic and a pleasure to read.

Sked, Alan & Cook, Chris
Post-War Britain: A Political History
Penguin pbk £8.99
0140179127

This is a long, detailed but accessible account of British political history from the general election of 1945 and the entry into office of Attlee's Labour administration to the Tory ousting of Margaret Thatcher in favour of John Major. The narrative outlines clearly the domestic political developments of the period and the recurring economic and social problems for which different governments proposed different solutions. It also examines closely Britain's changing role in international affairs.

Stevenson, John & Cook, Chris
Britain in the Depression
Longman pbk £12.99
0582229413

First published in the seventies under the title *The Slump*, this is a fully revised edition of a penetrating and acute examination of British politics and society in the thirties, a decade in which the country struggled with the consequences of recession, depression and mass unemployment. On its first publication one reviewer described it as 'one of the most relentlessly brilliant studies of twentieth century Britain yet published' and it remains the best analysis of the period in print.

Taylor, A.J.P
English History 1914 - 1945
Oxford UP pbk £9.99
019285268X

Taylor's account of these years is enlivened by his characteristic wit and gift for enlightening subversion of conventional interpretations. During ten of the thirty-one years under survey in this work the English people were involved in world wars; for nineteen of them they lived in the shadow of mass unemployment. These realities and the politics which sprang from them shape the narrative of a book which, despite the volume of work and research on the period carried out since the last revision of Taylor's text, remains a classic study of the interwar years.

Timmins, Nick
The Five Giants
Fontana pbk £8.99
0006863183

In his wartime report Sir William Beveridge pinpointed the obstacles that stood in the way of a successful post-war rebuilding of society. 'Want', he wrote,'is one only of five giants on the road to reconstruction.....The others are Disease, Ignorance, Squalor and Idleness.' Timmins' book shows how Beveridge's plans for defeating these giants blossomed into the Welfare State that emerged under the Attlee government, and assesses the key figures involved in its creation and the problems it has faced from its beginnings.

Ziegler, Philip
London at War 1939 - 1945
Mandarin pbk £7.99
074931625X

For long periods of the war London was a city under siege from the air and ordinary people found their lives violently transformed by the struggle with Nazi Germany. Drawing on interviews, unpublished letters and diaries, Ziegler has produced a telling social history and a fascinating record of how people responded to the dangers and pressures of wartime.

Irish History

Brown, Terence
Ireland : A Social and Cultural History 1922 - 1985
Fontana pbk £8.99
0006860826

Ireland was a state born in violence and divided from its birth by bitter quarrels. As a consequence, for many decades, it was a state that attempted to impose a notable degree of conformism on the social, cultural and educational institutions it introduced. Brown divides his study of the inevitably intertwined social and cultural history of the country into three. He in turn examines the first ten years of the Irish Free State, with its conservative continuity with pre-revolutionary Ireland, the years between 1932 and 1958 in which that continuity, despite the social and cultural evidence of major change in the making, was remarkably sustained, and the decades from 1958 to 1978 in which striking change occurred, made more striking by the contrast with what had gone before. Throughout the book Brown returns to telling consideration of important topics - nationalism, religion, censorship, language revival - and assesses the major literary and artistic achievements of the period.

Cahill, Thomas
How the Irish Saved Civilization
Hodder pbk £6.99
0340637870

This book examines the role of Irish monks in protecting Christian and pagan manuscripts during the Dark Ages. After the collapse of the Roman Empire and the sacking of Rome by the Visigoths, it was only the diligence of the Irish that preserved many classical texts that would otherwise have been lost. Cahill's book is engaging and lively, a fascinating account of a neglected corner of European history.

Coogan, Tim Pat
De Valera
Arrow pbk £9.99
0099958600

De Valera is the most important figure in 20th century Irish history. From the Easter Rising of 1916, in which he commanded the third battalion of Irish Volunteers in the doomed but heroic insurrection, through the anguish of the Anglo-Irish Treaty and the Civil War, to the extraordinary period of political power he enjoyed, he was the decisive figure in shaping, defining and (often) dividing the new Irish nation. Tim Pat Coogan's

gripping and intelligent biography is a remarkable study of the man and the long shadow he cast.

Coogan, Tim Pat
The IRA
Fontana pbk £8.99
0006384013

Coogan's account of the Irish Republican Army looks at its origins in the Irish Volunteers of the 1916 Easter Rising and follows it through the War of Independence and the bitter Civil War which ensued. He examines the stagnant years between the wars, when the IRA faced total suppression in the Irish Free State, and the series of bungled operations in the Second World War when they flirted with German intelligence. He analyses the Border Campaign of the fifties and the split in the sixties which led to the formation of the two wings, Official and Provisional, before devoting much attention to the Troubles in Northern Ireland during the last twenty eight years. This is a monumental book which tries to explain the history, role and purpose of the IRA, its long fight for a 32 county Irish republic and the terrible tragedies that have ensued.

Foster, Roy
Modern Ireland 1600-1972
Penguin pbk £9.99
0140132503

An engrossing and erudite study of Irish history from 1600, when the last great Gaelic counter-attack under Hugh O'Neill, Earl of Tyrone, was challenging the imposition of Englishness, to 1972. When it was first published in 1988, Foster's book met with great acclaim. Conor Cruise O'Brien said that, 'It supersedes all other general accounts of modern Irish history' and Owen Dudley Edwards stated that, 'With this book Dr. Foster becomes one of Ireland's greatest historians.' The strength of Foster's book is that it not only surveys the events of Irish history over nearly four centuries but that it also relates how those events acted upon people living in Ireland to produce eventually an 'Irish Nation' that, politically, was rooted in reality rather than rhetoric.

Falls, Cyril
Elizabeth's Irish Wars
Constable pbk £9.95
0094772207

Elizabeth I and her governments faced a continuous threat from Spain during her reign but there was another threat nearer home that drained her treasury and exhausted her armies - Ireland. Between 1560 and 1602 only superior military might, allied to a policy of ruthless subjugation, preserved English rule during a succession of rebellions throughout Ireland. Many of Elizabeth's foremost professional soldiers saw service in Ireland, Essex and Mountjoy amongst them. Ireland also found her heroes in leaders such as O'Donnell, Fitzmaurice, Tyrone and O'Neill. Spain schemed to keep the pot boiling and thus England's attention focused away from the continent. Cyril Falls' book has been republished for the first time in twenty years and once again takes its place as the best account available of Elizabeth's attempts to subdue Ireland and of the bloody campaigns which ensued.

Foster, Roy (ed)
Oxford Ilustrated History of Ireland
Oxford UP pbk £13.99
0192852450

The Oxford Illustrated Histories have a deservedly high reputation and this presentation of Irish history from prehistoric times to the present is readable and accessible. Produced by a team of leading Irish scholars, it is a vivid and authoritative history which is ideal for the general reader. The book focuses on the patterns of settlement and colonization, the recurring religious confrontation and the gradual emergence of new political models which have characterised the often troubled history of Ireland. Its central themes and arguments are illustrated with detailed reference to landscape, artefacts, architecture and contemporary visual reference.

Reproduced from *The Oxford Illustrated Encyclopedia of World History Vol. 2 (Oxford)*.

Irish History

A brief look at some of the many titles available on the history of Ireland

In few countries are the past and present so inextricably linked as in Ireland. The work of interpreting the past is also the work of re-defining and re-assessing the present. In the past few decades many gifted historians have undertaken these two tasks and the amount of work in print is too vast to be encompassed by a brief essay. For every title mentioned there are several more equally deserving of attention. The most substantial work of the last ten years, in every sense of the word, is the **New History of Ireland**, published by Oxford UP in what will eventually be ten volumes. Planned and established by the late T.W. Moody this series is the work of more than seventy scholars and is the definitive history of Ireland through the centuries. Unfortunately, at prices ranging from £60.00 to £90.00 a volume in hardback, it is, perhaps, beyond the pocket of all but the wealthiest devotee of Irish history. A multi-volume history which is more afford-able is produced by the Dublin publisher Gill & Macmillan. The first in the series is **Medieval Ireland** (0717116166 £12.99) and each of the subsequent volumes covers a particular century - **Sixteenth Century Ireland** (0717116239 £14.99), **Seventeenth Century Ireland** (0717116263 £14.99), **Eighteenth Century Ireland** (0717116271 £14.99), **Nineteenth Century Ireland** (0717116212 £14.99) and the final volume **Twentieth Century Ireland** (017116247 £14.99) which looks in detail at the estab-lishment and development of the independent Irish state.

Several one-volume histories of Ireland are reviewed separately in the section on Irish history but there are others which are worthy of attention. **A History of Ireland** (Routledge 0415048885 £11.99) by Peter and Fiona Somerset Fry is a comprehensive account which spans the entire period from the Neolithic age to the present day. **The Course of Irish History** (Mercier Press 1856351084 £13.99) by T.W. Moody is a well-known and long-established survey which has been recently revised, enlarged and updated. **The Making of Modern Ireland** (Faber 0571180361 £9.99) is a scholarly and challenging account of the cen-turies from 1603 to 1923. Sean McMahon's book **A Short History of Ireland** (Mercier Press 1856351378 £8.99) is a bold attempt to encompass the whole history of the island in 250 pages.

There are many valuable books which focus on particular periods and particular topics in Irish history. **Ireland in the Middle Ages** (Macmillan 0333606205 £10.99), by Sean Duffy, looks at the island's his-tory in the first half of this millennium, placing the English invasion at the heart of its survey and tracing the pre-invasion back-ground. **Ireland Since 1800** (Longman 058200473X £14.99), by Theodore Hoppen, is a textbook which is aimed primarily at undergraduates but, with its combination of chronological and thematic approaches to the major issues of the period, it is an enlightening work for other readers. D. G. Boyce is a well-respected scholar of Irish history and the author of the volume on the nineteenth century in the Gill & Macmillan series. His work **The Irish Question and British Politics** (Macmillan 0333665309 £9.99) is a searching analysis of the problems of modern Ireland, from the 1860s to the present day, set in the context of the wider history of the British Isles. **Ireland in the Twentieth Century** (Macmillan 033356796X £9.99) by D.W. Harkness charts the antagonisms that have divided Irish Nationalists from Irish Unionists throughout the century.

One of the central, traumatising events of Irish history was the Great Famine of the 1840s. As well as the classic account by Cecil Woodham-Smith (see page 66) a number of other books are worth consulting. Easily accessible and well illustrated is the volume in the New Horizons series, **The Irish Famine** (Thames & Hudson 0500300577 £6.95), by Peter Gray. More substantial and detailed are two works by Christine Kinealy - **This Great Calamity** (Gill & Macmillan 0717118819 £17.99) is a major survey of the famine and its effects and **The History and Ideology of the Great Irish Famine** (Pluto Press 0745310745 £12.99) questions the accepted notions of the inevitability of the famine and argues that more could have been done to mitigate the suffering. Another of the great agonising upheavals in Ireland's recent past is, of course, the Civil War. Calton Younger's major account of the war is, sadly, out of print but two other books that remain in print are **Green Against Green** (Gill & Macmillan 0717116301 £14.99) by Michael Hopkinson and **The Irish Civil War** (Wolfhound Press 0863274803 £6.99) by Helen Litton. The former is a good narrative account and the latter is a brief but well-illustrated review of the hostilities and internecine struggles.

Finally, no survey, however brief, of books on Irish history can ignore the individual figures, the heroes and anti-heroes (often the same person played both roles) of the nation's troubled past. Biographies of Parnell, Lord Edward Fitzgerald and De Valera are reviewed in the main section on Irish history. **Wolfe Tone** (Yale UP 0300051956 £12.95), by Marianne Elliott, is a definitive biography of the founder of Irish Republican nationalism which, in its careful examination of his personal life and public actions, reveals the truth that lies behind a heavily mythologised figure. As well as Robert Kee's **The Laurel and the Ivy** (see page 65), two other books on Parnell are worth consulting. **Parnell in Perspective** (Routledge 0415067235 £12.99), edited by George Boyce and Alan O'Day, is a collection of essays which examines many aspects of the nineteenth century politician's often enigmatic career. **Parnell** (Gill & Macmillan 071711886X £6.99) by Paul Bew is a short but authoritative biography which attempts to explain some of the paradoxes apparent in the life of a man who was a wealthy Protestant landlord and yet led a largely Catholic land reform and nationalist movement. Another Irishman who has been hidden behind the myths created to memorialise, and sometimes demonise, him is Michael Collins and the recent film version of his life by Neil Jordan has increased the interest in the man. Tim Pat Coogan's **Michael Collins** (Arrow 0099685809 £9.99) is a major biography of the Irish nationalist leader whose murder in the Civil War increased his legendary status.

Kee, Robert
The Green Flag:
The Most Distressful Country
Penguin pbk £8.99
0140147586

The Green Flag:
The Bold Fenian Men
Penguin pbk £7.99
0140147608

The Green Flag:
Ourselves Alone
Penguin pbk £7.99
014014756X

This has some claims to be the most comprehensive and illuminating history of Irish nationalism available and, given Robert Kee's elegant and witty prose, it is certainly the most readable. In the first volume he poses the question 'Who are the Irish' and endeavours to answer it by ranging through Irish history from its beginnings to the Great Famine in the eighteen forties. The second book carries the story from the founding of the Fenian movement to the tragedy of the 1916 Uprising, and Kee concludes his trilogy with a close examination of the decisive years between then and 1923 which saw the emergence of the Irish Free State. The whole work amply justifies F.S.L. Lyons's description of it as 'a sympathetic epic.'

Kee, Robert
Ireland: A History
Abacus pbk £14.99
0349106789

First published in 1980 to accompany a major TV series, this has been revised to take into consideration more recent events in Ireland including the preliminaries to the 1994 ceasefire agreement. It is a well-illustrated and well-written introduction to the past that has shaped Ireland's present and has shaped current Irish views of the nation's history. As Conor Cruise O'Brien has written, 'it is to be warmly recommended to those who know little or nothing about Irish history but, also, especially to those who think they know a lot about it.'

Kee, Robert
The Laurel and the Ivy :
Charles Stewart Parnell and
Irish Nationalism
Penguin pbk £8.99
0140239626

Charles Stewart Parnell was the major figure in the movement for parliamentary reform that swept Ireland in the mid-nineteenth century. His commitment to Ireland and its people and their support for him were unquestioned until the scandal of his relationship with a married woman, Mrs O'Shea, was revealed. A campaign of slander and innuendo, orchestrated by the British establishment and enthusiastically aided by envious erstwhile colleagues, ensured his political downfall. Kee's book tells the story of Parnell's fall from grace and poses the questions about what might have happened to the Irish cause had scandal not engulfed him.

Lee, Joseph
Ireland 1912 - 1985
Cambridge UP pbk £18.95
0521377412

A major work on Ireland, North and South, in the twentieth century, this is a book that should be read by all those who wish to deepen their understanding of modern Irish history. Although primarily a political study, it argues that Irish politics can only be understood in the broad context of economic, social, cultural and intellectual history and that the Irish experience cannot be made comprehensible if viewed in isolation.

Lyons, F.S.L.
Ireland Since the Famine
Fontana pbk £10.99
0006860052

When this monumental study of Ireland in the years since the great famine of the 1840s was first published, the reviewer in The Irish Times described it as 'an incomparable survey of modern Irish history.' Its central theme is the political evolution of the Irish nation from the parliamentary campaigns for Home Rule in the nineteenth century, through the bitter divisiveness of the civil war and the compromises inherent in the creation of the Free State, to the separate developments of Eire and Ulster since. However Lyons is also alert to the economic and religious factors which have helped to shape Irish history and examines the cultural climate which could produce both a passionate nationalist like Patrick Pearse and a bitter exile like James Joyce.

O'Brien, Conor Cruise & Maire
A Concise History of Ireland
Thames & Hudson pbk £7.99
0500273790

Maire and Conor Cruise O'Brien have produced a lucid and succinct account of the troubled course of Irish history, plagued as it has been by political, religious and social divides. What Yeats called the 'four deep, tragic notes in Irish history' are given due prominence - the Catholic revolt in Elizabeth's reign which ended with the Protestant settlement of Ulster, the Battle of the Boyne, the revolutionary impact of events in France at the end of the eighteenth century and Parnell's fall from grace which effectively ended hopes of a parliamentary solution to Irish nationalist demands. However the book carries the reader from prehistoric times to the present century. The 'partition' resonates through modern Irish history and the O'Briens have portrayed its creation and the continuing complexities of the two countries with understanding and sensitivity in a book that the Irish Times described as 'an exhilarating performance, free from bias'.

Woodham-Smith, Cecil
The Great Hunger
Penguin pbk £8.99
014014515X

Perhaps no event in Irish history has had the enduring impact of the failure of successive potato crops that occurred during the period 1845 - 1849. Long remembered as the Great Hunger, the famine that ensued led to the deaths of countless thousands and the emigration of thousands more. The famine, the deaths and the diaspora left a legacy of bitterness that remains to this day. Cecil Woodham-Smith's book, first published in 1962, retains its freshness and tells the story of the Great Hunger and the stories of those who suffered, died or fled. It also looks at the apparent failure of any concerted efforts of famine relief by the government and the landlords.

Scottish History

Black, Jeremy
Culloden and the '45
Sutton pbk £9.99
0750903759
The truth about the 1745 rebellion against George II's rule has often been lost in the swirling mists of the romantic legends about Bonnie Prince Charlie that developed after the defeat of the Jacobite cause. Jeremy Black's thoroughly researched study examines the context in which the uprising took place and the sequence of events which culminated in the battle of Culloden. He also gives due weight to the seriousness of the uprising and the extent to which it represented a real threat to the Hanoverian dynasty.

Fraser, George MacDonald
The Steel Bonnets
HarperCollins pbk £9.99
0002727463
The Border Reivers were rustlers and outlaws who terrorised the Anglo-Scottish frontier four hundred years ago. This book tells the story of the great raiding families - the Armstrongs, the Grahams, the Maxwells and others - and the endless fighting of English and Scottish outlaw bands across the borderlands.

Laing, Lloyd and Jenny
The Picts and the Scots
Sutton pbk £9.99
0750906774
Who were the Picts and the Scots? This highly readable book presents the evidence for the origins of these two peoples and for the relationship between them and traces their historical development from the period of raids on Roman Britain to the formation of rival Dark Age kingdoms.

Lynch, Michael
Scotland: A New History
Pimlico pbk £10.00
0712698930
A single volume history of Scotland which spans twenty centuries from the Picts to the present day and covers all areas of Scottish life.

Mackay, James
William Wallace
Mainstream pbk £9.99
185158823X
William Wallace, never forgotten by the Scots, was recently brought to the attention of a wider audience in the, perhaps, unlikely form of a kilted Mel Gibson in the film *Braveheart*. Mackay's book is a lively and readable biography of a man who emerged from obscurity to raise and lead an army that defeated the forces of Edward I at Stirling Bridge. Wallace was later defeated at the battle of Falkirk and his life ended in execution at Smithfield. However his example was a potent one to such successors as Robert the Bruce in the battle against English domination and he has remained, throughout the centuries, a powerful symbol of Scottish independence.

Mackie, J.D.
A History of Scotland
Penguin pbk £7.99
0140136495
Mackie held the Chair of Scottish History and Literature at Glasgow University for many years and his book was first published in 1964. It has been extensively revised by Bruce Lenman and Geoffrey Parker and retains its position as a readable one-volume account of Scotland's history from its first emergence as a united nation to the present day. Mackie chronicles the growth of a people who have fiercely defended their own autonomy and have long pursued an economic, religious and constitutional development that has been independent of, although interwoven with, that of its neighbours.

Maclean, Fitzroy
Scotland : A Concise History
Thames & Hudson pbk £7.95
0500277060

'The Scots,' remarked a censorious English Member of Parliament in 1607, 'have not suffered above two kings to die in their beds these two hundred years.' He was exaggerating but Scotland's history has undoubtedly been a bloody one and often a confused and confusing one. In this short and well-illustrated account Sir Fitzroy Maclean, who was a distinguished diplomat and soldier and the author of the classic wartime memoir *Eastern Approaches*, provides a helpful guide through the twists and turns of Scottish history.

Prebble, John
Culloden
Penguin pbk £7.99
0140253505

Prebble reconstructs the battle and the months of brutality and repression which followed it. Half-starved, poorly led and forced to fight from ill-chosen positions, the Highlanders under Bonnie Prince Charlie proved easy targets for 'Butcher' Cumberland's men. The book movingly recounts the story of the sufferings of ordinary Scots men and women for a cause that was never theirs.

Prebble, John
Glencoe
Penguin pbk £7.99
0140028978

' You are hereby ordered to fall upon the rebels, the MacDonalds of Glencoe, and to put all to the sword under seventy'. This coldblooded order was ruthlessly carried out on 13th February 1692 when the Campbells slaughtered their hosts, the MacDonalds, in the massacre at Glencoe. Prebble gives a fine, popular account of this bloody incident which had wide repercussions and which, in retrospect, can be seen as the beginning of the destruction of the Highland way of life.

Prebble, John
The Highland Clearances
Penguin pbk £7.99
0140028374

In the aftermath of Culloden the Highlanders suffered at the hands of their own clan chiefs. They were deserted and then betrayed into famine and poverty. While the chiefs grew rich, the people died of cholera and starvation or, evicted from the glens to make way for sheep, were forced to emigrate. Prebble's book remains the best popular retelling of the shabby story.

Prebble, John
The Lion in the North
Penguin pbk £6.99
0140056459

Eleven centuries ago Kenneth the Hardy emerged victorious from a series of savage battles as the ruler of a united Scotland. From that time until Charles Edward Stuart saw Jacobite hopes crushed forever on the battlefield of Culloden, the 'long brawl of Scottish history' was fought to its bitter conclusion. This account of that long brawl looks at the turbulent years of Scotland's independence, at the treachery and the idealism and the fierce self-sufficiency of the clans.

Smout, T.C.
A History of the Scottish People
Fontana pbk £9.99
0006860273
A Century of the Scottish People
Fontana pbk £9.99
0006861515

These two volumes cover the history of Scotland from 1560 until 1950.

Scottish History

A brief selection of more titles on Scottish history

For those wishing to investigate Scottish history in greater detail than that offered by a one-volume survey, the New History of Scotland published in eight volumes by Edinburgh University Press is essential reading. Beginning with Alfred Smyth's **Warlords and Holy Men** (0748601007), which covers the period from Roman incursions into Scotland to the year 1000, the series concludes with Christopher Harvie's sombre account of twentieth century history, **No Gods and Precious Few Heroes** (0748603875). The other volumes in the series are **Kingship and Unity : 1000 - 1306** (074860104X), **Independence and Nationhood : 1306 - 1469** (0748602739), **Court, Kirk and Community : 1470 - 1625** (0748602763), **Lordship to Patronage 1603 - 1725** (074860233X), **Integration and Enlightenment 1746 - 1832** (0748603859) and **Industry and Ethos 1832 - 1914** (0748601023). All the titles in the series are £9.95. Another valuable multi-volume series, which charts social change and development in Scotland and the growth of urbanisation and industrialisation in the period from the 18th century to the present, is published by the Edinburgh-based firm John Donald. Edited by well-known Scottish historians such as T.M.Devine and Rosalind Mitchison, the three volumes of **People and Society in Scotland** (Volume One 0859762106; Volume Two 0859762114; Volume Three 0859762122) are published under the auspices of the Economic and Social History Society of Scotland and each volume costs £16.00.

Some of the historians who have contributed to these series have also produced particular studies of Scottish history that have been paperbacked and make interesting reading. **Clanship to Crofter's War** by T.M.Devine (Manchester UP 0719034825 £14.99) charts the social transformation of the Highlands from the Jacobite Rising of 1745 to the great crofter's rebellion of the 1880s and he has also edited a collection of pieces on **Scotland in the 20th Century** (Edinburgh UP 0748608397 £14.95) which throws light on Scotland's experience of a period of unprecedented change. **The Great Highland Famine** (John Donald 0859763722 £22.00) is an examination of the acute famine which gripped Scotland at the same time as the much better-known catastrophe in Ireland. Christopher Harvie's book **Scotland and Nationalism** (Routledge 0415090415 £13.99) is an examination of nationalist aspirations in Scottish society and politics over more than two centuries. Other recent works which provide significant insight into their subjects are R.C.Paterson's **For the Lion** (John Donald 0859764354 £9.95), a history of the Scottish Wars of Independence and Stephen

Boardman's **The Early Stewart Kings** (Tuckwell Press 1898410437 £14.99), a joint biography of Robert II and Robert III, the two kings who established Scotland's most durable royal dynasty.

Other great figures of Scottish history have been the subjects of fine biographical and historical studies accessible to the non-academic reader. In addition to James Mackay's book (see page 67), **William Wallace** by Andrew Fisher (John Donald 0859761541 £8.95) is an established account of the often shadowy life of one of Scottish history's greatest heroes. The man who, perhaps, benefited most from Wallace's achievements is the subject of G.W.S. Barrow's **Robert the Bruce and the Community of the Realm of Scotland** (Edinburgh UP 0852246048 £15.95) which has been through a number of editions. Mary, Queen of Scots is the subject of one of Antonia Fraser's justly popular historical biographies (see page 27) and Rosalind Marshall's **Queen of Scots** (HMSO 0114931224 £7.95) is a well illustrated work on the same ill-fated Queen. The life of her consort Lord Darnley, victim of one of the most famous unsolved murders in history, is recounted in **Darnley** (Phoenix 1857997794 £9.99), recently in paperback. **Rob Roy MacGregor** by W.H. Murray (Canongate 0862415381 £5.99) brings together new interpretations of the life and times of a man who became a symbol of Scotland. Another character who has almost become lost amongst the mythologising is Bonnie Prince Charlie. Rosalind Marshall's study, published like her book on Mary in conjunction with the National Portrait Gallery of Scotland (HMSO 0114934207 £8.50) is a beautifully illustrated book which attempts to get at the man behind the myth and Sir Fitzroy Maclean's biography (Canongate 0862415683 £5.99) is a vivid account of his struggle to rally the clans and restore the Stuart monarchy.

Finally a one-volume history of the nation with a difference - The Baron of Ravenstone's **Scotland, Bloody Scotland** (Canongate 0862411165 £4.99) is a romp through the centuries of Scotland's past which is irreverent, accompanied by a series of light-hearted cartoons, but informative. No visitor to Scotland should be without it and every native might learn something new about his or her heritage.

Welsh History

Davies, John
Hanes Cymru
Penguin pbk £11.00
0140125701
History of Wales
Penguin pbk £9.99
0140145818

Originally published in Welsh as *Hanes Cymru* and later translated by Davies himself into an English work, this is a volume that spans the broad sweep of Welsh history from the earliest days to the present, from the end of the Ice Age to the miners' strike but does so with a scrupulous attention to detail and to the particular. By stripping away the myths that have so often gathered around the Welsh past in a work that nonetheless takes seriously the history of the Welsh as a people, Davies has created what one enraptured reviewer desribed as 'the greatest book of Welsh history ever written'.

Davies, R.R
The Age of Conquest
Oxford UP pbk £8.99
0198201982

One of the volumes of the History of Wales published by Oxford University Press in conjunction with the University of Wales, this is a detailed political and social history of Wales in the crucial centuries in which the English imposed their rule on the nation. Beginning at the end of the eleventh century and the struggle against the Norman invaders, Davies traces the transformations in Welsh society over the following 350 years and the troubled relationship with its more powerful neighbour.

Davies R.R.
The Revolt of Owain Glyn Dwr
Oxford UP pbk £9.99
0192853368

Owain Glyn Dwr was one of the most remarkable figures in Welsh history and the leader of the last sustained rebellion the Welsh mounted against the domination of the English. Born in the mid-fourteenth century, Glyn Dwr was acclaimed Prince of Wales in September 1400 and, although his revolt ended in a defeat made inevitable by the forces ranged against him, he succeeded in establishing a measure of Welsh unity beyond any previously experienced and creating, both for his contemporaries and succeeding generations, a vision of Wales as an independent country. Davies' book is the most recent study of this charismatic leader, who continued to evade the clutches of the English until his death, and of the social and political background to the rebellion which he led.

Morgan, Kenneth O.
Wales 1880 - 1980
Oxford UP pbk £8.99
0198217609

'This book will serve as a fulcrum of historical debate for a generation.' So wrote the well-known historian Gwyn Williams when this account of modern Welsh history was first published. Morgan guides the reader through the years of the Liberal ascendancy in the country before the First World War, through the period of economic hardship in which new Labour allegiances developed, to the dramatic changes and reborn sense of national identity in the last forty years. However his work encompasses more than just political and economic history, examining as it does all aspects of modern Wales from the social and religious to the literary and the sporting.

Williams, Gwyn
When Was Wales?
Penguin pbk £7.99
0140136436

'Wales is impossible. A country called Wales only exists because the Welsh invented it. They had no choice...And a hard time they had of it.' Professor Emeritus at University College, Cardiff and the author of numerous works on subjects as diverse as Medieval London, Goya, and the rise of communism in Italy, Williams has created an impassioned work useful to both scholar and general reader. The book begins with a poem by RS Thomas, and Williams continues throughout the book to draw on a diverse range of artistic, religious and political sources to create the story of Welsh national identity with authority, a masterful grasp of historical detail, and a profound sense of pride. His ability to integrate the significance of mythology and poetry into the history does much to engage the reader, as does his accomplished style. He never, however, strays into sentimentalism, and this is a rigorous and scholarly work beginning in the years before the first Roman invasions and continuing to the present day and what the author descibes as the 'dismantling' of a nation.

Welsh History

A selection of further titles on the history of Wales

The history of Wales, although inextricably linked for many centuries with that of its more powerful and aggressive neighbour, retains its own distinctiveness and there are a number of books and series of books in print which acknowledge that distinctiveness. On Medieval Wales there are a number of general texts, in addition to the volume in the Oxford History of Wales (see page 71). **Medieval Wales 1064 -1521** (Macmillan 033354773X £9.99), in the British History in Perspective series, examines themes in Welsh history from the coming of the Normans to the fall of the Duke of Buckingham in 1521 and looks particularly closely at the role of the leaders of the native Welsh community after Edward I's conquest of the land. **Wales in the Early Middle Ages** (Leicester UP 0718512359 £18.99) is an academic work in a series called Studies in the Early History of Britain but is accessible to the non-academic reader with a particular interest in the period.

Moving forward into the period of the late Middle Ages and the Tudors, Glanmor Williams' volume in the Oxford History, **Renewal and Reformation** (Oxford UP 0192852779 £9.99), is a comprehensive history of the two decisive centuries which followed the defeat of Owain Glyndwr, drawing extensively on the evidence to be found in the literature, prose and verse, Welsh and English. **Wales and the War of the Roses** (Sutton 0750909226 £18.99) by H.T. Evans is a reissue of a classic work, which surveys the military campaigns in Wales and the Marches, together with new illustrations and a valuable new introduction by Ralph Griffiths. **Tudor Wales** (University of Wales Press 0708309712 £8.95) edited by Trevor Herbert and Gareth Elwyn Jones is one of a useful series, Welsh History and its Sources. The British History in Perspective series from Macmillan includes a second volume on Welsh history, **Early Modern Wales c.1525 - 1640** (0333552601 £9.99), edited by Gwynfor Jones, which examines the main trends in Wales during the century following the Tudor settlement of the land.

Volume Four in the Oxford History of Wales **The Foundations of Modern Wales** (0192852787 £8.99) by Geraint Jenkins covers the years from 1642 to 1780, from the Civil War to the beginnings of the Industrial Revolution. The Welsh History and its Sources series has two useful volumes on **The Remaking of Wales in the Eighteenth Century** (0708310133 £8.95) and **People and Protest 1815 - 1880** (0708309887 £8.95) which looks at the series of social protests that periodically struck Regency and Victorian Wales. A book which looks more closely at one of these protest movements is David Williams' **The Rebecca Riots** (University of Wales Press 070830933X £10.95), an examination of the agrarian discontents of the eighteen forties in which men, disguised as women, took the law into their own hands.

Finally there are two excellent histories of Wales which cover extensive periods of time. **Modern Wales: A Concise History** (Cambridge UP 0521469457 £14.95) by Gareth Elwyn Jones deals with Wales from its days as a pre-industrialized society dominated by the landed gentry, through the transformations wrought by the Industrial Revolution, which had a particular impact on certain areas of the country, to the difficulties and challenges of the present day. Philip Jenkins's book **A History of Modern Wales** (Longman 0582489253 £17.99) is a substantial text which analyses Welsh society, its language, culture and religion, over four centuries from 1536 to 1990.

General European History

Cussans, Thomas
Times Atlas of European History
Times Books Hbk £25.00
0723006016
This is a major atlas which encompasses the entire history of the continent in a sequence of accessible and clearly laid-out maps, each provided with concise and lucid commentary. The maps explain not only how the Europe of today has been formed but make clear the forces that have moulded the Europe of the past, from the emergence of the first Greek city-states to the break up of the Soviet Empire.

Davies, Norman
Europe : A History
Oxford UP hbk £25.00
0198201710
This one-volume history of Europe, for all its imposing bulk, is intended to be read cover to cover, rather than used for reference. It requires a considerable commitment from the reader, but more than rewards that concentration. Its evenness of tone, organisation of material and control of narrative is impressive, and it is enlivened by Davies' dry humour. At first glance, the ambitious structure would seem to preclude a

straightforward read; twelve chapters follow the grand lines of European History, increasing in magnification as we near the present. Embedded in these chapters are hundreds of capsules, close focus augmentations of the text. These allow attention to be drawn to a variety of specifics which otherwise would be lost or would find no place in the narrative. These capsules do not disrupt the narrative flow of the text, even if read as they appear in the course of reading. They serve to illuminate the whole. This is a thoroughly engaging history which avoids the bias of Eurocentrism and 'western civilization'. It is an excellent place to begin looking at our past anew.

Delouche, Frederic
Illustrated History of Europe
Weidenfeld pbk £14.99
0297834088
An ambitious attempt to encompass the history of Europe from the earliest cave-painters of prehistory to the fall of the Berlin Wall, this book is the collective work of twelve historians from twelve different nations. Its insistence on a broader view of European history than the purely national informs its treatment of such subjects as the spread of Christianity, the wars of religion

and the years of revolution and its many illustrations and maps provide further information for the general reader at whom it is aimed.

Fernandez-Armesto, Felipe
Times Illustrated History of Europe
Times Books Hbk £25.00
0723007241
This is a superbly produced book which tackles the history of Europe as a whole and explores the development of the European idea from prehistory to the present day. Switching deftly from lofty vision to sharp close-up, and making excellent use of some handsome illustrations, the book places particular and, in the context of recent history, apposite emphasis on the role of Eastern Europe in the continent's evolution.

Green, Vivian
The Madness of Kings
Sutton pbk £12.99
0750906812
A study of the ways in which the mental health of rulers throughout history, from Roman emperors to twentieth century dictators, has played a determining role in shaping historical events. Green shows how the personal traumas of such mon-

archs as Charles VI of France - who often believed, among less harmless delusions, that he was made of glass and would break if he fell - and Ivan the Terrible of Russia - whose grotesque cruelties included sewing the archbishop of Moscow in a bear skin and having him hunted to death by hounds - had disastrous impacts on the countries they governed. Green writes with wit and humour and his anecdotes of insanity hold an appalling fascination, but his book is also a serious attempt to provide a new perspective on the understanding of historical processes and to acknowledge how much the mental illnesses of individual rulers affected their decision-making and their public policies.

Hufton, Olwen
The Prospect Before Her
Fontana pbk £9.95
0006863515

In the last thirty years the emergence of the history of women as a field of enquiry, and the production of much fine work designed to restore women to the historical record by focusing on their lives and experiences, have been amongst the most exciting developments in historiography. Olwen Hufton's monumental book synthesises and distils the work of many scholars into a volume which advances our understanding of how women in Western Europe lived their lives in the three centuries between 1500 and 1800. She discusses the different stages of women's lives - girlhood, work, marriage, motherhood, widowhood - and examines the experiences of those who, by chance or design, failed to conform - prostitutes, witches, nuns, saints, early feminists.

McEvedy, Colin
Atlas of Medieval History
Penguin pbk £7.99
0140512497

Covering the period from the reign of Constantine in the fourth century to the great voyages of discovery in the 15th century which opened up the medieval world, McEvedy's atlas treats as one unit Europe, the Mediterranean and the Central Asian steppes from which the Huns, Turks and Mongols emerged. Through maps and accompanying commentary, he traces the shifting political, religious and economic developments in this large region.

McEvedy, Colin
Atlas of Modern History
Penguin pbk £7.99
014051153

This atlas, covering Europe in the years since 1815, is the concluding volume in a set of four which use the same formula of a chronological sequence of maps to illustrate historical trends and developments. Using a simple map of the continent as the base, McEvedy shows Europe at a succession of particular dates, detailing those political and military developments which can be readily expressed in geographical terms. Each map is faced by a page of clear and concise explanatory text.

Williams, E.N.
Penguin Dictionary of English and European History
Penguin pbk £8.99
0140510842

This dictionary provides the essential information on the leading figures, events and ideas of the early modern period from the accession of Henry VII to the throne of England to the outbreak of the French Revolution. Although there are, necessarily, references to the cultural and social history of the period, the emphasis is firmly on the political and there are entries on all the major people who held power in Europe, from Charles I of England to the Holy Roman Emperor Charles V, from the Borgia Pope Alexander VI to Thomas Wolsey.

Ancient Greece

Andrewes, Antony
Greek Society
Penguin pbk £8.99
0140138285

Andrewes' book is a well-established introduction to the basic and distinctive features of Greek society in the late archaic and classical periods looking at the lives of the landowners and peasants, the traders, craftsmen and slaves who made up that society. This is a comprehensive and readable study of the social history of the civilisation which fought off the threat of Persian invasion in 480 B.C. and which, before it tore itself apart in the internecine struggles of the Peloponnesian war, created many of the cornerstones for Western culture since.

Arrian
Campaigns of Alexander
Penguin pbk £7.99
0140442537

Arrian was a Greek who enjoyed a successful career in the Roman army of the second century A.D. His account of Alexander's campaigns is of particular value because he based it on first hand accounts to which he had access.

Boardman, John (ed)
Oxford History of the Classical World : Greece and the Hellenistic World
Oxford UP pbk £9.95

This collection of essays by a number of classical scholars, including Peter Levi and Robin Lane Fox, provides a comprehensive view of the achievements and the history of the Greek city-states, from their emergence in the eighth century B.C. to the conquests of Alexander the Great. Chapters on political and social history are interspersed with introductions to Greek drama and Greek myth, to Homer and to Aristotle and Plato.

Burn, A. R.
Penguin History of Greece
Penguin pbk £9.99
0140137513

Combining accessibility with erudition, this balanced but vivid account of centuries of Ancient Greek history is, in many ways, the best one-volume treatment of its subject. Burn provides an engaging narrative of the history of Hellas from the time of Mycenaean civilization, through the splendours and successes of fifth century Athens to the dramatic conquests of Alexander the Great and the decades of turmoil which followed his death.

Bury, J.B. & Meiggs, Russell
History of Greece
Macmillan pbk £16.99
0333154932

The first edition of Bury's History of Greece was published in 1900 and successive revisions have meant that it has retained its position as the basic introduction to its subject for generations of undergraduates. The revisions by Russell Meiggs are wide-ranging, made in the light of the enormous amounts of new work done and new evidence unearthed this century, but great care has been taken to preserve the basic character of the original and the scale and emphasis of Bury's account of Ancient Greece from the earliest centuries to the death of Alexander.

Chadwick, John
Decipherment of Linear B
Cambridge UP pbk £6.95
0521398304

Linear B was the name given to a system of writing found on clay tablets at Mycenaean palace sites. It remained undeciphered until Michael Ventris, who had trained as an architect but had long been interested in the problem, devoted much time to analysis of the texts and, in 1952, came to the conclusion

Fox, Robin Lane
Alexander the Great
Penguin pbk £8.99
0140088784

Alexander the Great only lived for 32 years, but left behind him an empire of over two million square miles and a personal mythology so great that it becomes extremely hard to disentangle legend from fact. So little irrefutable evidence remains from his life that Fox exhorts us to be wary of any text claiming absolute authority for any so-called documentary evidence. Having said as much however, Fox manages to demonstrate both great scholarship and the capacity to dissect all the entangled layers of conflicting information with considerable delicacy and apparent objectivity. He helps the reader beyond the centuries of misquoted and attributed information that tend to cloud any real sense of Alexander ever having been mortal. Additionally, Fox demonstrates an enviable capacity to interpret information, giving the reader great psychological insight into a man who combined a towering passion for Greek culture with military ambitions of giddying scale. Winner of three major literary prizes on publication in 1973, the book continues to be one of the best and most absorbing accounts of this ancient king, and a great insight into a complex personality.

that the script was an early form of Greek, a view subsequently confirmed by other scholars. Ventris died tragically young but his great achievement is made clear in this book by his close collaborator, John Chadwick, which both traces the evolution of Ventris' ideas and offers a brief survey of late Minoan and early Mycenaean archaeology.

Finley, M.I.
The World of Odysseus
Penguin pbk £6.99
014013686X

Who was Homer and when were the Iliad and the Odyssey composed? From what sort of society did the epic tales of Odysseus, Achilles and the Trojan War emerge? What were the beliefs that society held about government, religion, class and sex? Moses Finley was one of the most distinguished historians of the ancient world and a writer who could combine erudition with accessibility. In this book he used both the evidence of the texts and the evidence of archaeology and anthropology to reconstruct the Homeric world.

Fox, Robin Lane
Pagans and Christians
Penguin pbk £12.00
0140159894

When, in the early years of the fourth century, the Emperor Constantine, by a series of actions, made Christianity the principal religion of the empire, Christians did not constitute, by a long way, the majority of his subjects. A variety of pagan religions had devotees throughout Constantine's empire and paganism continued to exert influence for a long time after Constantine's death. Robin Lane Fox's book draws on a vast array of sources to produce a fascinating picture of the interplay and interaction between pagan religions and Christianity in the Roman Empire. He examines how Christianity came to command the support of the Emperor, how it assimilated pagan beliefs into its own and how it formulated a concept alien to pagan religions, that of heresy. Lane Fox's erudition, his gifts as a writer and the broad canvas on which he works, combine to make this one of the most rewarding studies of the ancient world to be published in the last twenty years.

Alexander the Great

A selection of titles on
Alexander of Macedon

Regarded as a god in his own lifetime, the model for future imperial conquerors from Caesar to Napoleon, and the subject of many fantastic legends, Alexander of Macedon continues to exert a fascination on those who have studied his extraordinary career. In the section on Ancient Greek history we have reviewed two biographies by distinguished scholars, Peter Green and Robin Lane Fox, and the Penguin Classics edition of Arrian, probably the most reliable of the ancient historians who wrote on Alexander. However there is a wealth of other titles on the man and his times available. Penguin Classics also publish the **History of Alexander** (0140444122 £8.99), by the Roman historian Quintus Curtius Rufus, which is a readable and lively account, drawing indiscriminately on both bad and good sources, and an edition of **The Greek Alexander Romance** (0140445609 £8.99), a hotchpotch of materials deriving from stories written in Egypt in the second century A.D. which was the basis for knowledge of Alexander throughout the Middle Ages. Plutarch's **The Age of Alexander** (Penguin 0140442863 £8.99) is a selection from his Parallel Lives of nine biographies of Alexander and his contemporaries.

Perhaps the most original of recent studies is John Maxwell O'Brien's book **Alexander the Great: The Invisible Enemy** (Routledge 0415106176 £11.99) which focuses on the central role alcohol played in Alexander's life, exploring Dionysus as a symbol of the destructive effects drink had on his psyche. **Conquest and Empire** (Cambridge UP 052140679X £7.95), by A.B.Bosworth, is an admired survey of Alexander's career and the battles and campaigns which marked his passage of the known world from the banks of the Danube to the banks of the Indus. N.G.L. Hammond is an eminent classicist who has written a history of Macedonia and has contributed to the Oxford Classical Dictionary and the Cambridge Ancient History. **Alexander the Great: King, Commander and Statesman** (Bristol Classical Press 185399068X £13.95) is a revised edition of a biography which made extensive use of the extant literary sources. A less academic work is **Alexander the Great: The Heroic Ideal** (Thames & Hudson 0500300704 £6.95) which is one of the compact, highly illustrated series of books called New Horizons.

The Generalship of Alexander the Great (Da Capo 0306803712 £11.95), written by J.F.C. Fuller, one of the foremost military historians of this century, is a reasoned assessment of his remarkable abilities as a commander of troops. Donald Engel's book **Alexander the Great and the Logistics of the Macedonian Army** (University of California P. 0520042727 £11.50) is a detailed but rewarding analysis of the methods by which Alexander's armies, far away from their homelands for long periods of time, were supplied and maintained. Finally, a book published recently by Routledge, **The Greek World in the Fourth Century** (0415105838 £14.99), edited by Lawrence Tritle, is a collection of essays which examine closely the Greek world into which the rapidly emerging power of Macedon under Alexander and, before him, his father Philip II, erupted.

Green, Peter
Alexander of Macedon
University of California Press pbk
£13.95

Because of the paucity of direct information about Alexander's life and the difficulties of interpreting what little there is, there has been much controversy and disputation between modern scholars of his startling career as general and empire-builder. Green's achievement is to weave that into an exciting and coherent narrative of Alexander's life. He strips away the romantic legends that began to accumulate around Alexander from the time of his early death in 323 B.C. and reveals a portrait of a complex but ruthless tyrant whose ambition for absolute power, and determination to achieve it, led eventually to his estrangement from reality.

Green, Peter
A Concise History of Ancient Greece
Thames & Hudson pbk £6.99
0500271615

Green provides an authoritative and witty study of Greece during the centuries which preceded the Hellenistic age. Among other topics, he discusses the culture of Minoan Crete, Mycenaean civilization as it appears in the Homeric tradition and in historical fact, the rise and fall of the city-states and the roles within them of some of the tyrants and lawgivers, the poets and philosophers whose names have come down to us. Much more than just a narrative of political events and military campaigns, his book draws an entertaining picture of many facets of Greek culture and history.

Herodotus
Histories
Penguin pbk £7.99
0140446389

Herodotus (c.480 B.C. - c.425 B.C.) is often referred to as the 'father of history,' since he was the first to collect material systematically and to make some effort to assess its accuracy. His work describes the long struggle between Greece and Asia in the two hundred years immediately before his own birth and includes descriptions of the Persian expeditions of Darius and the Greek victory at Marathon.

James, Peter
The Sunken Kingdom
Pimlico pbk £8.99
0712674993

The story of Atlantis has fascinated many people since Plato first wrote about a mysterious island continent, the centre of a rich civilisation, which disappeared in the depths of the seas. Scholars have tried to discover the archaeological and historical truth behind Plato's story ; theorists, of varying degrees of crankiness, have constructed fantastic edifices on the foundations of what he wrote. Peter James, who wrote *Centuries of Darkness,* a book which postulated major scholarly misinterpretation of the chronology of ancient history, argues that Plato's tale does have a basis in fact. However Atlantis could not have been in the Atlantic nor could it have been the volcanic island of Santorini. Careful analysis of the sources reveals that the original for Atlantis was a major Bronze Age city in Western Turkey which was destroyed by an earthquake and submerged beneath a lake.

Morkot, Robert
Penguin Historical Atlas of Ancient Greece
Penguin pbk £9.99
0140513353

Western civilization has its source in the creativity and energy of the Ancient Greeks and this atlas, in more than sixty colour maps, charts the development of their diverse cultures, from the Minoan civilization of Crete, through the Persian Wars and the artistic glories of the golden age of Athens, to the conquests and empire of Alexander the Great.

Plutarch
Age of Alexander
Penguin pbk £7.99
0140442863
Rise and Fall of Athens
Penguin pbk £6.99
0140441026

All the Penguin volumes of Plutarch's works in print are taken from his *Parallel Lives*, biographies of eminent Greeks and Romans often written in pairs as a means of comparison of the subjects. Although often unreliable, because of his wish to point a moral or exemplify a particular vice or virtue, Plutarch is rich in anecdote and gives vivid descriptions of significant historical events. He was a popular author in the Renaissance and was a significant source for Shakespeare's Roman plays.

Kitto, H.D.F.
The Greeks
Penguin pbk £6.99
0140135219

According to Kitto, in his introduction to this classic work first published in 1951, the Greeks 'had a totally new conception of what human life was for, and showed for the first time what the human mind was for.' In the rest of his passionate and insightful exploration of the culture and history of Classical Greece, of the life of the people who inhabited its city-states, he sets out to amplify and justify this claim.

McEvedy, Colin
Atlas of Ancient History
Penguin pbk £7.99
0140511512

his reference work illustrates, in a chronological sequence of maps, the evolution and flux of races and civilizations in Europe, the Mediterranean world and the Middle East from 50,000 B.C. to the fourth century A.D. The rise and fall of many peoples, from the Egyptians to the Romans, from the Hittites to the Ancient Greeks are clearly delineated.

Radice, Betty
Who's Who in the Ancient World
Penguin pbk £8.99
0140510559

For the last twenty years this has been the leading reference work for non-classicists to the classical world and the ideal means of fostering a basic knowledge of the Greek and Roman worlds. Radice covers not only the major figures in Greek and Roman history, the emperors, tyrants and generals who shaped events, but also the figures of legend and mythology who have continued to appear and re-appear in Western literature over the centuries. This is the definitive guide to the living past of the classical world.

Thucydides

**The History of the
Peloponnesian War**

Penguin pbk £7.99
0140440399

Thucydides (c.460 B.C. - C.395 B.C.) is the leading source for our knowledge of the Peloponnesian War, the struggle between the two city-states of Athens and Sparta in the fifth century B.C., and one of the most important of ancient historians. In his concerns with accuracy and exactness and in his determination to explain history in human terms, without recourse to the gods or fate, he approaches more nearly than any other ancient historian to a concept of history recognisable to us.

Wood, Michael

In Search of the Trojan War

Penguin pbk £7.99
0140238700

Michael Wood's book is a fresh and readable examination of the historical truth behind the most enduring stories in Western literature - the abduction of the beautiful Helen, wife of Menelaus, by a Trojan prince and the ten-year war between the Greeks and the Trojans which ensued. Did the Trojan War really take place and did the characters involved in it - Hector and Achilles, Agamemnon and Odysseus - really exist? Wood follows in the footsteps of those who have tried to locate the legendary city and focuses particularly on the pioneering work of Schliemann at Troy and Mycenae and Arthur Evans who uncovered the unsuspected riches of Minoan civilization when excavating at Knossos in Crete.

Xenophon

A History of My Times

Penguin pbk £7.99
0140441751

The Persian Expedition

Penguin pbk £7.99
0140440070

An Athenian and a disciple of Socrates, Xenophon (c.428 - c. 354 B.C.) led an adventurous early life before banishment by Athens and the provision of a country estate by the Spartans provided him with the leisure to undertake his extensive and varied writings. *The Persian Expedition* is his account of the march into Persia of a Greek force under Cyrus, the disastrous battle in which Cyrus and most of the Greek generals were killed and the epic retreat of the surviving Greeks, largely under the leadership of Xenophon himself, back to the coast and safety. *A History of My Times* covers the last years of the Peloponnesian War, the rise of Sparta and the rivalry in 4th century Greece between Thebes and Sparta.

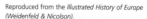

Reproduced from the *Illustrated History of Europe*
(Weidenfeld & Nicolson).

Ancient Rome

Appian
The Civil Wars
Penguin pbk £8.99
0140445099

Appian was a Greek lawyer of the 2nd century A.D. who wrote, in Greek, narratives of Roman wars and conquests from the earliest times to the reign of Vespasian. This Penguin Classics selection from his surviving work gives a vivid portrait of the epoch from the time of the Gracchi to the struggle for power following the murder of Julius Caesar, a struggle that only ended when Augustus defeated Antony and Cleopatra.

Boardman, John (ed)
Oxford History of the Classical World : Rome
Oxford UP pbk £9.95
0192852485

The civilization of Ancient Rome, like that of Ancient Greece, has a special claim on the West since much of our own culture has grown so directly out of it. In this volume, extracted from the Oxford History of the Classical World, a number of distinguished scholars - including Jasper Griffin, Michael Crawford and Henry Chadwick - have combined to produce a book that throws much light on that civilization. Chapters dealing with social and political history, that tell the story of Rome's rise from a cluster of villages on the Tiber to a vast empire, are interspersed with chapters on literature and philosophy, on art and architecture, in this fascinating and beautifully illustrated volume.

Carcopino, Jerome
Daily Life in Ancient Rome
Penguin pbk £8.99
014012487X

Subtitled *The People and the City at the Height of the Empire*, this is a classic account of Roman life which moves from a general portrait of the social, cultural and religious activities of the city to a detailed depiction of everyday life, following the typical routine of a normal day from dawn to dinner.

Cary, M.
History of Rome
Macmillan pbk £16.99
0333278305

Cary's history was first published in 1935 and was extensively revised by H.H. Scullard in 1974 to include the new evidence, both archaeological and epigraphic, that had come to light and the enormous amount of scholarly work on the subject that had been published in the interim. It continues to be a standard textbook on the whole period of Roman history from the semi-legendary foundation, usually dated to 753 B.C., through the conquest of Italy, the wars with Carthage to establish domination of the Mediterranean world, the internecine struggles of the late republic and the centuries of imperial rule up to the time of Constantine.

Dudley, Donald
Roman Society
Penguin pbk £8.99
0140136843

This is an excellent, succinct narrative of Rome's history from its semi-legendary beginnings until the death of Constantine. Dudley reviews the main historical events which shaped Roman society over the centuries and also provides a sound introduction for the general reader to the art and architecture, literature and philosophy, law and commerce of the people with the best claim to be considered the founders of Europe.

Gibbon, Edward
The Decline and Fall of the Roman Empire Volume
Penguin pbk £15.00
0140433937

The Decline and Fall of the Roman Empire Volume 2
Penguin pbk £15.00
0140433945

The Decline and Fall of the Roman Empire Volume 3
Penguin pbk £15.00
0140433953

The Decline and Fall of the Roman Empire : A One Volume Abridgement
Penguin pbk £7.99
0140431896

'It was at Rome....as I sat musing amidst the ruins of the Capitol, while barefoot friars were singing vespers in the Temple of Jupiter, that the idea of writing the decline and fall of the city first started to my mind.' Thus Gibbon (1737 -1794) described the genesis of his monumental work which traces the history of the Roman Empire (in its widest definition) from the time of Trajan through the reigns of successive emperors, through the division of the empire in two, through the rule of Charlemagne in the West and the long history of the Eastern empire, to the capture of Constantinople by the Turks in 1453. Gibbon's narrative skill, his detached and elegant prose and his vast erudition and careful use of the sources available to him, have meant that his work retains its value both as literature and as a history which later scholarship has built upon rather than entirely superseded. The three-volume edition in Penguin Classics is recently published and was described in the TLS as 'the best text we have ever had.'

Josephus
The Jewish War
Penguin pbk £8.99
0140444203
Josephus (A.D. 37 - c.98) was a Jewish general in the campaigns during the revolt in Judaea against Roman domination but, after a period of imprisonment, survived these to settle in Rome, become a Roman citizen and write, in Greek, an account of the events of the revolt, many of which he had witnessed himself. The book ends with a moving description of the siege of Masada and the mass sucide of its Zealot defenders when they realised that all hope of continued Jewish resistance to Rome was gone.

Livy
The Early History of Rome
Penguin pbk £8.99
0140441042

Rome and Italy
Penguin pbk £6.99
0140443886

Rome and the Mediterranean
Penguin pbk £8.99
0140443185

War with Hannibal
Penguin pbk £9.99
014044145X
Livy (59 B.C. - A.D. 17) was the author of an immense history of Rome from the earliest times to the civil war which followed the death of Julius Caesar and the reign of Augustus, who became Livy's patron, despite the historian's republican sympathies. Only thirty five of the original 142 books of Livy's history survive but they include his accounts of the legendary origins of the Roman state and the struggles between Rome and Carthage in the Second Punic War. Although uninterested in much that modern historians would consider essential to his project, Livy remains enormously readable and his use of dramatic set-pieces and lively characterisation is memorable.

Meier, Christian
Caesar
Fontana pbk £9.99
0006863493

Julius Caesar is remembered in
the popular imagination for his
involvement with Cleopatra and
the manner of his death on the
Ides of March. In fact, his career
spanned several of the decades
in which the Roman Republic
struggled to survive the contradictions inherent in its political
system and the crises which
these provoked. He was a member
of the Triumvirate which
governed Rome from 59 B.C.,
he spent many years in the
conquest of Gaul and he
emerged victor from the civil
war with his fellow triumvir
Pompey which raged from 49-45
B.C. The autocratic powers
which he exercised from the
time of Pompey's defeat and
death provoked the conspiracy
of disaffected aristocrats which
resulted in Caesar's assassination
in 44 B.C. This recent biography
places Caesar's career of brilliant
and ruthless opportunism firmly
in the context of a political
system in decline.

Peddie, John
The Roman War Machine
Alan Sutton pbk £10.99
0750910232

Peddie provides a solid account
of Roman military organisation
and tactics, drawing on first-
hand sources to give his work a
refreshing breadth of focus, covering both the more glamorous
aspects of generalship and
weaponry and the logistical and
operational techniques of the
army, essential but less readily
reconstructed from the evidence. He also makes some
striking and illuminating com-
parisons between Roman procedures and more modern military
campaigns, such as Burma in
1944, in a book which makes a
good case for the sophistication
of the Roman command and
control system.

Plutarch
Makers of Rome
Penguin pbk £7.99
0140441581

Fall of the Roman Republic
Penguin pbk £7.99
0140440844

These two volumes of brief
biographies, drawn from the
Parallel Lives of the first century
Greek writer Plutarch, include
accounts of the lives of Caesar,
Pompey and Cicero. Often
unreliable as historical evidence,
Plutarch's work is nonetheless
rich in anecdote about its subjects' personal and public lives.

Polybius
**The Rise of the Roman
Empire**
Penguin pbk £8.99
0140443622

Polybius (c. 200 - 118 B.C.) was a
Greek historian who spent many
years in Rome and acted on a
number of occasions as an inter-
mediary between the expanding
Roman empire and the declining Greek city-states. His history,
of which only a portion survives,
is an attempt to explain the
events which, in a brief period of
time, led to Rome's domination
of the Mediterranean world.

Reproduced from the *Illustrated History of Europe*
(Weidenfeld & Nicolson).

Pomeroy, Sarah B.

Goddesses, Whores, Wives and Slaves

Pimlico pbk £10.00
0712660542

What were the roles of women in Greek and Roman society? When pagan goddesses were at least as powerful as gods, why was the status of women generally so low? Pomeroy provides answers to these and other questions in this important book which ranges across 1500 years of classical antiquity, from the fall of Troy to the death of Constantine, and draws on both literary and archaeological evidence to reconstruct the lives of women from all classes of society.

Sallust

The Jugurthine War/The Catiline Conspiracy

Penguin pbk £6.99
0140441328

Sallust (86 - 35 B.C.) had an adventurous early career in politics and was an associate of Julius Caesar before retiring from public life to write the historical monographs for which he is remembered. The *Jugurthine War* is an account of Roman campaigns against a troublesome king of Numidia; the *Catiline Conspiracy* tells the story of Catiline, a disreputable politician, a near-contemporary of Sallust, who, after various intrigues against the state, led his followers into an open and disastrous rebellion which resulted in his death.

Scarre, Chris

Penguin Historical Atlas of Ancient Rome

Penguin pbk £9.99
0140513299

The Roman Empire was the first great multinational state in history and its physical and intellectual legacy have been major formative influences on the development of Europe. This atlas, in more than sixty colour maps, traces its rise and fall, examining closely its provinces and cities, its armies and frontiers, its foreign wars and internal conflicts, charting its transformation into a Christian theocracy and the incursions of 'barbarian' armies which brought about its downfall.

Scullard, H.H

From the Gracchi to Nero

Routledge pbk £12.99
0415025273

This has long been established as the standard text on Roman history in the period from the time of the brothers Tiberius and Gaius Gracchus and their attempted reforms of the Republic, through the decline and fall of the Republic, to the establishment of the Pax Romana under the early emperors. Scullard provides a comprehensible narrative of these confused and confusing times - the rivalries of the two generals and politicians Marius and Sulla, the period of Caesar's domination of the state, the creation of the principate under Augustus - and also presents chapters on the social and economic history of the period, and on its art and literature.

Suetonius

The Twelve Caesars

Penguin pbk £7.99
0140440720

Suetonius (A.D.c.70 - c.140)
was the author of a number of
highly indiscreet and highly
entertaining biographies of the
first twelve Roman emperors.
Writing in the time of a new
dynasty of rulers, Suetonius felt
no need to present the members of previous dynasties as
moral heroes and his portraits
of Tiberius, indulging his sexual
fantasies in retirement at Capri,
of Caligula, grotesque and
insanely cruel, and of Nero,
histrionically and egotistically
fiddling whilst Rome burned,
are memorable if not always
reliable.

Tacitus

The Annals of Imperial Rome

Penguin pbk £7.99
0140440607

The Histories

Penguin pbk £7.99
0140441506

Tacitus (c.A.D. 55 - 117)
was the greatest historian of
Imperial Rome and his *Annals*
and his *Histories,* although they
survive only in part, reflect
his grasp of the major political
issues of the time, his undis-
guised preference for the
republican rather than the
imperial past, and his desire to
use history to inculcate virtue
and hold up vice for posterity's
condemnation. The surviving
parts of the *Histories* cover the
two years A.D. 69 and 70, a period he describes as 'full of catastrophe, fearful in its fighting,
torn by mutinies, bloody even
in its peace.' The *Annals,* again
incomplete in the form in
which they have reached us,
cover the period from the death
of Augustus to that of Nero.

Reproduced from the *Illustrated History of Europe*
(Weidenfeld & Nicolson).

Middle Ages

Barber, Malcolm
The New Knighthood
Cambridge UP pbk £8.95
0521558727

This is a soundly researched overview of the warrior monks known as the Knights Templar and is the distillation of Barber's work on the subject over many years. The book fills the gap that has existed between very academic works and the cranky, semi-hysterical accounts that abound because of the nature of the dissolution of the order and the trials for heresy and burnings that resulted. Charting the order, from its origins in 1119, through its occasionally glorious successes and its spectacular defeats in the Holy Land, to its eventual demise, Barber reviews the nearly two hundred years of its existence in meticulous detail and with scrupulous attention to the source material. Moreover he offers what other historians of the order have not done - a brief exposé of the conspiracy theories which have circulated in one form or another since the abolition of the Order of the Temple in 1307.

Barber, Malcolm
The Trial of the Templars
Cambridge UP pbk £7.95
0521457270

The warrior monks of the Order of the Temple amassed great wealth during the Crusades but, after 1291 and the expulsion of the Christians from Palestine, they became vulnerable to the attacks of those, particularly Philip IV of France, envious of this wealth. In 1307 the Templars in France were arrested and charged with a variety of heresies and abominations. The Pope, initially reluctant, was drawn into instructing other European rulers to arraign the Templars. This book is a detailed examination of the long sequence of trials that followed, of the confessions made under torture, of the Templars' efforts to defend themselves and of the ultimate suppression of the order. Barber has written what is the standard account of this medieval *cause célèbre*.

Bartlett, Robert
The Making of Europe
Penguin pbk £9.99
0140154094

Conquest and colonisation are usually thought to be characteristic of the centuries after the discovery of the Americas, when Europe expanded and the great empires of Spain, Portugal and, later, Britain were created. In this ground-breaking work, Bartlett argues that the centuries between 950 and 1350 saw the forging of an increasingly homogeneous society, the 'Making of Europe', in a period of great expansionary activity. States were established by conquest and distant countries on the peripheries of the continent were peopled by waves of immigrants from the heartlands. The English colonised the Celtic world, German settlers moved deep into Eastern Europe and the Spanish recovered much that had been lost earlier to Islamic powers. By concentrating on these movements and by asking what developments in law, language and belief accompanied the warfare and the settlement, Bartlett gives the reader an original and stimulating perspective on the history of Europe in the High Middle Ages.

Cohn, Norman
The Pursuit of the Millennium
Pimlico pbk £12.50
0712656642

Throughout the Middle Ages prophecies of a millennial paradise, a kingdom of the saints in which humanity would be freed from the burdens of sin and suffering, periodically seized the imaginations of large groups of people. Often expectations of miraculous transformations of the world were coupled with social unrest, and movements threatening to the social hierarchy developed. Cohn's book is an original and powerful study of some of these movements, from the men and women who processed through the villages and towns of 13th century Italy and Germany, beating themselves and mortifying their bodies in the hope of gaining spiritual redemption, to the extraordinary messianic reign of John of Leyden over the German town of Munster.

Davis, Ralph
A History of Medieval Europe
Longman pbk £15.99
0582494001

Davis's book, which covers the period from Constantine in the 4th century to Saint Louis in the 13th century, is a standard introduction to the period for students. Split into two parts, the first spanning the Dark Ages and the second the High Middle Ages, it includes chapters on such subjects as the barbarian invasions, the Carolingian empire and the medieval church and papacy, all written in a clear and concise style.

Eusebius
The History of the Church
Penguin pbk £8.99
0140445358

Bishop of Caesarea in Palestine, Eusebius (A.D. 265 - 340) wrote his ecclesiastical history in Greek and it is the earliest source for historians wishing to reconstruct the development of the early church from its foundation to the later part of Eusebius' life.

Frayling, Christopher
Strange Landscape
Penguin pbk £6.99
0140261249

Based on a well-received TV series, this is Frayling's journey through the strange landscape of medieval life and culture. In his introduction he draws attention to the ways in which versions and echoes of the Middle Ages continue to permeate our popular culture, from fantasy games to the novels of Ellis Peters. In successive chapters, he proceeds to map out some of the features of the medieval landscape, as he studies the creation of the great cathedrals of France, the contrasting fates of the challenging doctrines of the Cathars and of St.Francis, the confrontation between the mystic St. Bernard of Clairvaux and the philosopher Abelard, and the ideas about love and religion revealed in Dante's Divine Comedy.

Froissart
Chronicles
Penguin pbk £7.99
0140442006

Froissart (c.1337 -c.1410) was a French chronicler and poet who travelled widely in medieval Christendom to gather material for his accounts of the chivalric exploits of the nobility of France and England during his lifetime. His lively writings are an important, although unreliable, source for historians of the Hundred Years' War.

heart of Russia, Viking soldiers serving Byzantine emperors and the Viking mariners who sailed to North America are all tracked in the pages of a handbook useful to both the student and the general reader.

Gimpel, Jean
The Medieval Machine
Pimlico pbk £10.00
0712654844

The basic argument of this book by the renowned medievalist Jean Gimpel is that the commercial and industrial capacity of the Middle Ages has been seriously underestimated. Drawing on a wide range of source material he shows how the people of the period applied considerable inventiveness and ingenuity to agriculture, light industry and building.

Haywood, John
Penguin Historical Atlas of the Vikings
Penguin pbk £9.99
0140513280

The traditional picture of the Vikings is one of lawless marauders descending upon defenceless communities to rape and pillage. This atlas, in more than sixty colour maps, shows how limited a picture this is and charts the activities of the Norsemen as traders and craftsmen, explorers, settlers and mercenaries. Viking merchants travelling into the

Holmes, George
Oxford Illustrated History of Medieval Europe
Oxford UP pbk £15.00
0192852205

This richly illustrated book tells the story of Europe during the thousand years which saw the creation of western civilization. Written by expert scholars and drawing on the latest research, it offers a lively and authoritative account of life in medieval Europe between the fall of the Roman Empire and the dawn of the Renaissance. From Charlemagne to the Hundred Years War, the story includes the rise of the monasteries and the building of the great cathedrals, the Crusades and the clash between Christendom and Islam, the catastrophe of the Black Death and the growth and development of towns and cities, of trade, commerce and banking. Over 200 illustrations, maps and genealogies amplify the text.

Huizinga, Johan
The Waning of the Middle Ages
Penguin pbk £8.99
0140137025

Huizinga (1872-1945) was a Dutch scholar of prodigious learning and this cultural history, first translated in 1924, remains a stimulating account of

the end of the Middle Ages and the beginning of a new era. It has necessarily been overtaken by the huge body of scholarly work that has taken place since its publication but its classic status seems assured and it has been compared, with only slight exaggeration, to a vast canvas which 'like the great altarpieces of the brothers Van Eyck, contains a prodigious variety of detail and yet does not detract from the main central theme of the picture.'

Reproduced from The Oxford Illustrated History of Medieval Europe (Oxford).

The Vikings

A selection of further titles on the culture and achievements of the medieval Norsemen

The image of the Vikings in the popular imagination - the blood-thirsty pirates descending on defenceless communities to burn and pillage - is a gross simplification. As the wide-ranging studies of Roesdahl (see page 92) and Gwyn Jones (see page 89) demonstrate, the Vikings were a vital and creative people whose skills as navigators and explorers were matched by their talents as artists and craftsmen. In 1980 a BBC TV series, presented by Magnus Magnusson, did justice to the reality of Viking culture and the book of the series **Vikings!** (BBC 056336453X £14.95) continues to offer a highly illustrated survey of the life of the Norsemen. **Atlas of the Viking World** (Facts on File 0816030049 £22.95) is a well-produced reference work that includes dozens of maps and colour illustrations. **The English Heritage Book of Viking Age England** (Batsford 0713465204 £13.99) provides a synthesis of knowledge of the Vikings in England, with a particular emphasis on information gleaned from recent archaeological work. New Horizons is a series of compact but highly illustrated introductions to a wide range of historical and artistic subjects. Yves Cohat's **The Vikings: Lords of The Seas** (Thames & Hudson 0500300151 £6.95) is one in the series.

Some of the more academic studies of the Vikings are accessible to the non-specialist with a particular interest in the subject. **The Vikings in Britain** (Blackwell 063118712X £7..99) by Henry Loyn is one of a series, Historical Association Studies, of short but incisive investigations of particular topics. **The Vikings in History** (Routledge 0415083966 £12.99) by Donald Logan is a scholarly reassessment of the Vikings which looks at their transformation from seafaring raiders to assimilated settlers. **Kings and Vikings** (Routledge 0415045908 £13.99) by P. H. Sawyer offers new interpretations of the development of Scandinavian societies and the conversion from pagan to Christian in the Viking Era. Two studies of specific topics, **Women in the Viking Age** (Boydell Press 0851153607 £12.95) by Judith Jesch, and **Towns in the Viking Age** (Leicester UP 071851792X £16.99) by Helen Clarke and Bjorn Ambrosiani, offer interesting perspectives on the period.

In the last analysis perhaps the best way to approach Viking society and Viking culture is through those later Norse writers who recorded the mythology of their people and the heroic deeds of their predecessors. Not only are the sagas enjoyable and entertaining as stories, but they contain a wealth of incidental detail which reveal the everyday lives and beliefs of the Norse people and the colonists who settled in Iceland, Greenland and North America. Snorri Sturluson (1178 - 1241) was the most important figure in Old Icelandic literature and the **Edda** (Dent 0460876163 £5.99) his best -known work. Sturluson was, in all likelihood, also the author of **Egil's Saga** (Penguin 0140443215 £6.99), the biography of a Viking poet and other sagas of approximately the same period are published by Penguin. **The Orkneyinga Saga** (Penguin 0140443835 £6.99) is the history of the Norse Earls of Orkney and **The Vinland Sagas** (Penguin 0140441549 £5.99) is a collection of the earliest records of the adventurousness of the Viking voyagers as they sailed ever further westwards.

Jones, Gwyn
A History of the Vikings
Oxford UP pbk £9.99
019285139X

When this book was first published one reviewer described it as 'the most brilliantly written, balanced and explanative general work on the Vikings ever to appear in English.' Jones charts the civilization and culture of the Viking realms from the origins of the Norsemen in legend to the defeat of Harold Hardrada at Stamford Bridge in 1066, the effective end of the political power of the Vikings, if not of their cultural influence. He also investigates Viking exploits in war, trade and colonisation, looks at their far-flung contacts with the Slav and Muslim worlds and traces their voyages to settle Iceland, Greenland and America.

Jones, Terry
Crusades
Penguin pbk £6.99
0140257454

Were the Crusades an honourable quest to spread European Christianity or an excuse for the crusading knights to grab valuable lands in the Middle East? Terry Jones, with Alan Ereira, brings an irreverent and refreshing but nonetheless scholarly approach to the bloody history of the Crusades, a history which ranged from the high horror of the Jerusalem massacre in 1099 to the low farce of early crusaders besieging a castle defended only by sheep. This is as lively and as entertaining a book as one would expect from someone with Terry Jones's credentials as well as a reliable analysis of the motives and actions of participants on both the Christian and Muslim sides.

Keen, Maurice
Penguin History of Medieval Europe
Penguin pbk £7.99
0140136304

An introduction for the general reader who knows little of the Middle Ages but would like to know more. Keen illuminates the great themes of the period - the growth of trade and the shifting patterns of community life as villages grew into towns and towns into cities, how papal involvement in worldly politics blurred the distinction between the temporal and the spiritual and how the Hundred Years War escalated from feudal dispute to national conflict. The book shows the central importance of the idea of the unity of Christendom and how, by the mid fifteenth century, that idea had been irreversibly undermined.

Kieckhefer, Richard
Magic in the Middle Ages
Cambridge UP pbk £10.95
0521312027

Covering the years from 500 to 1500, this book examines natural and demonic magic and its position in medieval culture. Adopting an interdisciplinary approach that combines history, religion and psychology, Kieckhefer argues persuasively that magic should not be seen as a fringe subject but rather as an area vital to an understanding of life in the period.

Le Goff, Jacques
Medieval Civilization
Blackwell pbk £15.99
0631175660

This survey of a thousand years of the history of Western civilization, written by one of France's most distinguished historians, has been acclaimed as both a scholarly and a popular classic. Part One is a narrative account of the entire period from the barbarian settlement of the Roman Empire to the close of the medieval period. Part Two is analytical, examining the origins of early medieval ideas of culture and religion and reconstructing the lives and sensibilities of people during this long period.

Leyser, Henrietta
Medieval Women
Phoenix pbk £9.99
1857997352
This social history of women
over the thousand years from
450 to 1500 draws on a large
body of research, undertaken
by many scholars over the last
twenty five years, to produce a
readable and fascinating portrait
of women's lives in the period.
It is divided into four sections.
Part One examines what the limited evidence can tell us about
women in the Anglo-Saxon era.
Part Two provides a brief snapshot of their lives in and around
the most famous date in English
history - 1066. Views of sex,
marriage and motherhood, the
world of work and the experience of widowhood in the High
and Later Middle Ages are
investigated in Part Three and
the book concludes with a study
of the intellectual and spiritual
worlds of medieval women
revealed by female monasticism,
and the by the lives of such lay
figures as Margery Kempe.

Lynch, John
The Medieval Church
Longman pbk £14.99
0582494672
The Church was the central
institution of the European
Middle Ages and the foundation
of medieval life. It transcended
national frontiers and national
jurisdictions, yet it affected the
individual, in all social classes,
on a regular basis and in the
most fundamental transactions
of his or her life. No aspect
of the medieval world or the
medieval world view was
untouched by its influence.
This one-volume survey, aimed
at both the academic and the
non-specialist, is a comprehensive history of the western
church, concentrating on ideas
and trends rather than personalities, examinining it in all the
varying roles it played within
medieval society.

Mayer, Hans Eberhard
The Crusades
Oxford UP pbk £12.95
0198730977
This one-volume history of
the Crusades is comprehensive
enough to serve the needs of
many undergraduates and
general readers and provides
an excellent introduction to the
subject for those intending to
move on to more detailed study.
Mayer is acute in his analysis
of those Western European
attitudes which inspired the
Crusades. His text reflects the
growing body of scholarly work
on the Crusader kingdoms and
the position of the kingdoms
in the broader context of the
Muslim world by which they

were surrounded for the two
centuries of their often precarious existence.

Neillands, Robin
The Hundred Years War
Routledge pbk £13.99
0415071496
Neillands, a gifted journalist,
travel writer and popular
historian, tells the story of the
longest war in European history,
a war which changed irrevocably
the two medieval nations
involved in it. The origins of
the conflict are assessed, the
great battles of Crécy, Poitiers
and Agincourt vividly described
and the remarkable saga of Joan
of Arc is succinctly portrayed in
a work that is the ideal introduction for the general reader.

Norwich, John Julius
**Byzantium: The Early
Centuries**
Penguin pbk £9.99
0140114475

Byzantium: The Apogee
Penguin pbk £9.99
0140114483

**Byzantium: The Decline
and Fall**
Penguin pbk £9.99
0140114491
John Julius Norwich's Byzantine
trilogy is a superb achievement
in narrative history which tells

the extraordinary story of the eastern empire through more than a thousand years. The volumes are rich in revealing anecdote and detail and offer concise and witty character sketches of the individuals, (a selection of largely appalling adventurers, drunkards, sinister eunuchs and deranged tyrants, leavened by the occasional saint and scholar), who people the compelling saga. Volume One carries the tale of the Roman Empire's second capital to the moment on Christmas Day 800 A.D when Pope Leo III crowned Charlemagne as a rival emperor to the one ruling in Byzantium. Volume Two takes the reader through the following three centuries and concludes with the coronation of the heroic Alexius Comnenus in 1081. The final volume charts the decline and fall of the empire from the accession of Alexius through the disastrous Fourth Crusade, when an army destined for the Holy Land was diverted to Constantinople, with predictably violent results, to the last struggle with the encroaching Ottomans and the terrible siege of 1453 which ended the empire. Few history books tell as gripping a story as these three volumes and even fewer tell so gripping a story so well.

Riley-Smith, Jonathan
**The Oxford Illustrated
History of the Crusades**
Oxford UP Pbk £14.99
01982852949

Riley-Smith has assembled a team of distinguished scholars to produce a volume which traces the history of the crusades from the preaching of the First Crusade, through the capture of Jerusalem and the establishment of the crusader states, through the Third Crusade and the confrontation of Saladin and Richard I, to the final fall of Acre in 1291. The result is a fascinating work, richly illustrated, with over 200 colour and black and white pictures, which introduces the general reader to the results of recent academic study of the Crusades and presents a comprehensive and authoritative survey of the extraordinary clash, over two centuries, of two cultures, Christian and Islamic. The book concludes with an intriguing examination of the legacy of crusading ideas and imagery in the modern world.

Reynolds, Susan
Fiefs and Vassals
Oxford UP pbk £14.99
0198206488

In this substantial volume, Reynolds sets out to provide a fundamental challenge to orthodox conceptions of feudalism. She argues that these derive, ultimately, from the works of medieval academic lawyers and that the ideas of the fief and of the vassalage, which post-medieval scholars have constructed from these sources, do not accurately reflect the realities of

medieval society. Her radical new examination of the relationship between rulers and ruled, between nobles and the freeborn, overturns many of the basic ways in which we have learnt to think about the Middle Ages.

Roesdahl, Else
The Vikings
Penguin pbk £8.99
0140125612

'For 300 years,' writes Else Roesdahl, 'from just before 800 until well into the eleventh century....the Vikings affected almost every region accessible to their ships, and left traces that are still part of life today.' In her broad survey, which brings together the latest research in all aspects of the Vikings from their art and poetry to their burial customs, she destroys the myth of them as nothing more than axe-wielding barbarians and pirates. She draws a compelling portrait of a creative people, who established complex

Reproduced from *The Oxford Illustrated History of Medieval Europe (Oxford)*.

social institutions, oversaw the coming of Christianity to Scandinavia and made a major impact on European history.

Runciman, Steven
History of the Crusades: The First Crusade
Penguin pbk £11.00
0140137068

History of the Crusades: The Kingdom of Jerusalem
Penguin pbk £11.00
0140137041

History of the Crusades: The Kingdom of Acre
Penguin pbk £12.00
014013705X

Sir Steven Runciman was the most distinguished historian of the Byzantine world in English this century and his writing was always wonderfully lucid and accessible. His *History of the Crusades* has long been a standard work. He described the tale of the Crusades as 'one of faith and folly, courage and greed, hope and disillusion' and his three volumes amply illustrate the conflicting emotions and motives that inspired the participants, both Christian and Muslim, in the period covered by his work. The first book covers the First Crusade, the capture of Jerusalem by the Christian knights and the subsequent establishment of the Kingdom of Jerusalem and other crusader states. In his second volume he describes the history of the kingdom in the years before the recapture of Jerusalem by Saladin in 1187, which led to the Third Crusade and the military confrontation of Richard the Lionheart and Saladin. The final part of the work examines the increasingly hard-pressed Crusader lands in the last century of their existence before the fall of Acre and the final expulsion of the Christians from the Middle East in 1291.

Seward, Desmond
The Monks of War
Penguin pbk £8.99
0140195017

Seward gives a clear and balanced account of the various religious orders that developed in the early middle ages and combined dedication to God with ruthless military prowess. The Templars and Hospitallers, created to defend the crusader Kingdom of Jerusalem and the pilgrims drawn to it, and the Teutonic Knights, who carved out a kingdom in the Baltic regions as they fought an indigenous population that was still pagan, are all examined. So too are the facts surrounding the much-debated downfall of the Templars and the epic struggles of the Hospitallers to retain a power-base in the Mediterranean, first at Rhodes and then at Malta.

Southern, R.W.
The Making of the Middle Ages
Pimlico pbk £10.00
071265688X

This broad and sweeping analysis of the social, economic and intellectual changes which shaped western Europe in the period between the late tenth and early thirteenth centuries demonstrates clearly how the continent and its position in the world were transformed during these years. As a reviewer wrote in the TLS, because of 'the power of Southern's prose, the breadth of his imaginative vision.....there is no questioning the greatness of *The Making of the Middle Ages*' and, more than forty years after first publication, it remains one of the indispensable books for all those interested in medieval history.

Tuchman, Barbara
A Distant Mirror
Papermac pbk £12.00
0333644700

During the middle years of the fourteenth century, the Black Death killed about a third of the population between India and Iceland. Although the most profound calamity to afflict that period, it was attended by many others; war, famine, taxes, and schism in the Church to name but a few. The God who presided over the world seemed a vengeful and punitive God. Many assumed the plague to be a second Flood. Tuchman's history focuses on the aftermath of the plague and it is anchored by one man's story, Enguerrand de Coucy, a French nobleman whose life and career act as our guide. The approach works well; Coucy is the ideal centre to the story as he played an important role in many of the key events of his time, as well as bridging the warring countries of England and France by virtue of his marriage to the king of England's daughter. Care is taken to demonstrate that normal life did prevail even in extreme circumstances and Tuchman is wary of the disproportionate survival of the negative in documentary evidence ('No Pope ever issued a Bull to approve of something'). Even so, through this long and absorbing history, there is little evidence of humanity's advancement, and much of disasters both inflicted and endured.

Wroe, Ann
A Fool and His Money
Vintage pbk £7.99
0099581817

Taking the records of the partitioned town of Rodez in the Languedoc and focusing upon a particular court case involving a crock of gold unearthed in a sewer in 1369, Ann Wroe has reconstructed, with great skill, life as it was lived in a particular place at a particular point in history. As accessible as a good novel, yet informed by extensive archival research, *A Fool and His Money* creates an unforgettable portrait of a divided town and the people who inhabited it.

Ziegler, Philip
The Black Death
Penguin pbk £7.99
0140152202

The Black Death was the name given to the virulent form of bubonic plague which swept into Europe from Asia in the fourteenth century and, by some estimates, carried off one in three of the population. So many people died that the resultant shortage of labour created social and economic unrest throughout Europe for decades. Ziegler's very readable book traces the progress of the epidemic through Europe and investigates such attendant phenomena as the Flagellants, groups of people roaming the countryside, beating and mortifying themselves in the hopes of appeasing God, and the pogroms of Jewish communities blamed for the appalling suffering inflicted by the disease.

Reproduced from *The Oxford Illustrated History of Medieval Europe* (Oxford).

Early Modern Europe

Bonney, Richard
The European Dynastic States
Oxford UP pbk £14.99
0198730233
One of the volumes in the Short Oxford History of the Modern World, this study of Europe in the sixteenth and seventeenth centuries is aimed at the student, but accessible to the committed general reader with a particular interest in the period. Bonney's central focus is on the dramatic upheavals and changes in politics, society and religion in the period which resulted in almost constant warring between the emerging states.

Braudel, Fernand
The Mediterranean and the Mediterranean World in the Age of Philip II Volume 1
University of California Press pbk £15.95
0520203089

The Mediterraneanan and the Mediterranean World in the Age of Philip II Volume 2
University of California Press pbk £15.95
0520203305
The product of decades of research this is one of the outstanding works from the school of French historians associated with the journal *Annales*. Braudel's approach to his mater-

ial - beginning with those forces, such as geography and climate, whose operation and effects exhibit themselves over stretches of time as long as their impact is profound - is such that he achieves a satisfying integration of rich and specific detail into a broad and overarching structure. In the first volume of his massive work he describes the geography and environment of the Mediterranean which shaped its subsequent history, the broad economic and social conditions which produced similarly broad historical trends, while his second volume brings his study to a powerful climax with the political and physical confrontation of the Hapsburg- Spanish and Ottoman empires at the Battle of Lepanto.

Burckhardt, Jacob
The Civilization of the Renaissance in Italy
Penguin pbk £8.99
014044534X
Burckhardt (1818 - 1897) was a 19th century Swiss historian, whose most famous work was first published in German in 1860. However his main thesis - that the Renaissance was the period in which men and women, previously only aware of themselves as members of 'a race, people, party, family or

corporation', became conscious of themselves as spiritual individuals - has remained both influential and highly controversial.

Cronin, Vincent
The Florentine Renaissance
Pimlico pbk £12.50
0712698744

The Flowering of the Renaissance
Pimlico pbk £12.00
0712698841
The Italian Renaissance was the first age to define and name itself. Its protagonists had a strong sense of starting anew, coupled with an affinity with the rediscovered classical past. Vincent Cronin divides his history into two main streams of development; the first book addresses the Quattrocento and Florentine ascendancy, the second follows the shift in focus to Rome and Venice in the 16th Century. The author meets the various imperatives of his task with elegance and clarity. He acknowledges the inequities of the period and the always uneasy alliance of renewed classical learning with Christianity. Those who contributed in numerous disciplines take their turn centre stage along with their patrons. Particularly well drawn is the

relationship between Pope Julius II and Michelangelo. This self-styled 'warrior pope', responsible for ejecting the French from Italy and for strengthening the Papal states, was also an enthusiastic patron of the arts, and was intent on restoring Rome to its former glory. Artists and architects of the calibre of Perugino, Lotto and Raphael were draughted in. Particularly memorable is Cronin's description of Michelangelo's first attempt at ceiling fresco; suspended under 10,000 square feet of chapel ceiling, blinded by dust and pigment, the harried artist was driven to descend repeatedly in search of additional funding for his work.

Doyle, William
The Old European Order 1660-1800
Oxford UP pbk £14.95
019820387X

This volume in Oxford's Short History of the Modern World covers the 140-year period which witnessed the beginnings of the modern world. Doyle's discussion of the economic and social structures of pre-revolutionary Europe, the ways in which government was organised and power distributed and the intellectual trends of the time, focuses on broad themes and developments and looks at the stresses and problems that led to a general crisis in the old order and the outbreak of revolution.

Englander, David
Culture and Belief in Europe 1450-1600
Blackwell pbk £13.99
0631169911

This collection of primary sources, intended to illustrate the relationship between cultural change and religious belief in 16th century Europe, was designed for an Open University course. The editors have chosen a wide range of material from political and philosophical writings, from plays and poems, diaries and letters and from writers such as Erasmus and Sir Thomas More, Rabelais and Sir Philip Sidney. The result is a reader of interest, not just to students of a particular course, but to all those interested in the period and its intellectual debates.

Hale, John
The Civilisation of Europe in the Renaissance
HarperCollins pbk £14.99
000686175X

This book, the most ambitious achievement of Britain's leading historian of the Renaissance, he himself describes modestly as 'an investigative impression' of the intellectual and cultural efflorescence that took place between about 1450 and 1620. This was the first age in which 'Europe' and 'European' became terms with a widely understood significance, an age which many of the people at the time thought of as unique, and an age which witnessed the emergence of new and pervasive attitudes to what were considered the most valuable aspects of civilized life. How did Europeans at the time see themselves and others? What did they call civilized? What did they buy and sell? How did they dress and eat? What did they think about and how did they communicate their thoughts? These are just some of the questions which John Hale considers in this exciting, powerful and beautifully illustrated book.

Hampson, Norman
The Enlightenment
Penguin pbk £8.99
0140137459

The philosophers of the Enlightenment, heavily influenced by the scientific revolution of the 17th century that was embodied by men like Descartes and Newton, sought to dispel the clouds of pessimism and superstition that had, as they saw it, hidden from men's eyes the progress possible through the application of reason. By the 1760s the initial optimism of the Enlightenment had developed into an ambiguous awareness of the uniqueness of the individual consciousness and its relation to the larger world. The stage was set for the revolutionary upheavals of coming decades and the rise of Romanticism. In this book Norman Hampson traces several dominant themes in the Enlightenment and describes the contemporary social and political climate in which they operated.

Jardine, Lisa
Worldly Goods
Macmillan hbk £25.00
0333638107

Most previous works on the Renaissance have concentrated on the fashioning of a new cultural identity in Europe during the period when the rebirth of classical scholarship combined with the work of great artists to produce a flowering of civilization. Jardine concentrates in great and illuminating detail on the material culture of the Renaissance - paintings, printed books, tapestries, precious gems, rich fabrics - and the determined competitiveness with which the noble and the wealthy vied with one another to possess these goods. Great works of art, she argues, were created in the context of ruthless struggles for commercial power. The 'new learning' was disseminated by publishing houses and printing presses established to take advantage of a new marketable commodity, the printed book. She offers a vivid picture of a world in transition and a new perspective on the Renaissance.

Levack, Brian C.
The Witch-Hunt in Early Modern Europe
Longman pbk £14.99
058208069X

In the centuries between 1450 and 1750, the secular and ecclesiastical courts of many European nations prosecuted many thousands of people, mostly women, for supposedly practising black magic and consorting with the Devil. Many unfortunates, again mostly women - and scholars debate fiercely about precise numbers - were burnt at the stake or otherwise lost their lives. Levack's carefully organised and readable book is a wide-ranging survey of this phenomenon and what lay behind it. It has proved a valuable addition to the literature on a topic which fascinates many people and which continues to engage the attentions of feminist historians, as well as medievalists and historians of religion.

Manchester, William
A World Lit Only By Fire
Papermac pbk £12.00
0333613473

This book began as an introduction to a biography of Ferdinand Magellan, the sixteenth century explorer, but assumed its own

life as a broad history of the period. The brutality of the age is strikingly realised; the 'fire' of the title burned fiercely on the bodies of dissenters and heretics. This occasionally unbalances the first part of the book as the reader is taken through a painstaking catalogue of barbarity. More successful is the central section which examines the fractures beginning to appear in the Catholic Church and Holy Roman Empire. Manchester illuminates the various stages in the development of this rift; the Borgia grip on the Papacy, Erasmus and the rise of Humanism, Luther raising the standard of reform and the unwillingness and subsequent inability of Rome to stem the tide. Which leaves the reader with Magellan. When he rounded the Straits of Patagonia in his crumbling ship, deserted by half his fleet, but firmly convinced he was nearing the end of his voyage, he entered the inconceivable vastness of the Pacific with half of his journey still to go, and it is this episode which stays in the mind long after the book is finished.

Parker, Geoffrey
The Thirty Years War
Routledge pbk £16.99
0415128838
The Thirty Years War was the central crisis in the history of early modern Europe. This new and revised edition of a much admired text incorporates the results of the latest research into a wide-ranging analytical account of the conflict which ravaged cental Europe. Geoffrey Parker, who has written extensively on the seventeenth century, and those fellow scholars who have contributed to the book, have produced a lively and judicious work which is useful to students and to interested general readers.

Plumb, J.H.
Penguin Book of the Renaissance
Penguin pbk £9.99
0140135898
This volume, first published in 1961, carries a considerable number of illustrations that help illuminate the text and is an excellent introduction to the religious, political and philosophical backdrops to the Renaissance. Plumb explores and offers his own analysis of

the achievements of the period, and his work is accompanied by individual essays from authors and historians such as Kenneth Clark, Hugh Trevor Roper and Jacob Bronowski. This is a very accessible and absorbing read; Plumb keeps the reader going at a good pace, and the contributed essays enhance rather than disturb the narrative flow of the book. Plumb and his fellow contributors demonstrate their historical insight and scholarly understanding and the book is highly recommended to any general reader looking for a reliable, introductory insight into the period. There is the added bonus of quite detailed portraits of key individuals of the time - Lorenzo de'Medici, Machiavelli, Pope Pius II and the young Michelangelo.

Tawney, R.H.
Religion and the Rise of Capitalism
Penguin pbk £8.99
0140184244
Tawney (1880 -1962) was a historian, socialist and teacher who was associated for many years with both the Workers' Educational Association and the London School of Economics, where he was professor of economic history. His best known work, which has rarely been out of print since publication in 1926, is a groundbreaking study of the interaction between religious beliefs and the social, political and economic developments which led to capitalism. Tawney's arguments have often been superseded by the work of later historians but the broad

sweep of his survey, from the Middle Ages to the early part of the eighteenth century, remains impressive and the book continues to engage readers.

Wedgwood, C. V.
The Thirty Years War
Pimlico pbk £12.50
0712653325
The Thirty Years War, which ravaged Central Europe in the years between 1618 and 1648, began as a religious conflict between Catholic and Protestant and developed into a bloody struggle between those who wished to extend the power of the Hapsburg dynasty and those who wished to limit it. Dame Veronica Wedgwood's classic account was first published in 1938 but, because of her command of the sources in several European languages and her elegant, precise prose, it retains its status as an important and relevant survey of the war.

Europe in the Age of Revolution and Empire

Blanning, T.C.W.
The Oxford Illustrated History of Modern Europe
Oxford UP Hbk £25.00
000198203748

Professor Blanning has gathered together eleven scholars of international repute to write this major history of Europe in the last two centuries. The beginning of the volume is the end of the eighteenth century because, as Blanning writes, 'it was then that revolution broke out in France, that the process of industrialization in Britain became visible to the naked eye, that the wars of the French Revolution and Napoleon brought change to every corner of the continent.' The story is carried forward through two hundred years of transformation to the break up of the Soviet Union and the sudden resurgence of nationalism which has brought new nation-states into being. Transformation - of the continent and indeed of the world, since, for much of the period, the world was caught in economic, social and cultural bonds created by Europeans or peoples of European descent - is, perhaps, the central theme of this incisive, entertaining and highly illustrated history which will give the general reader new insight into the Europe of the past and the present.

Gildea, Robert
Barricades and Borders
Oxford UP pbk £14.99
0198206259

One of the volumes in the Short Oxford History of the Modern World, this is a comprehensive survey of European history from Napoleon's assumption of power to the assassination of Franz Ferdinand and the outbreak of World War One. Gildea concentrates on the twin themes of revolution and nationalism that dominated the continent throughout the nineteenth century and deals also with the demographic and economic upheavals - massive increase in numbers and mobility of population, rapid industrialisation and expansion of markets - that changed the way many Europeans lived their lives.

Hobsbawm, Eric
**The Age of Capital
1848 - 1875**
Abacus pbk £10.99
0349104808

**The Age of Empire
1875 -1914**
Abacus pbk £9.99
0349105987

**The Age of Revolution
1789-1848**
Abacus pbk £9.99

The Age of Extremes
Abacus pbk £9.99
4349106711

Hobsbawm is widely acknowledged as one of our greatest historians - sensitive, subtle, and, as Ben Pimlott described him, the keeper of 'Olympian' erudition and knowledge. This magnificent four-volume exploration of the last two hundred years is one of the best possible introductions to a dramatic period of human history. From the French Revolution to two cataclysmic world wars, taking the reader through the history of Western Imperialism and the rise of capitalism, Hobsbawm covers great sweeps of history without ever loosing his grip of the details. That he achieves all this with wit, and a gentle, sane intellect explains the esteem in which this series of books is held. The last volume, *Age of Extremes*, is more personal - this is the age through which the author has himself lived. His insights are characteristically potent. Drawing together the threads of history that make up his vision of our troubled century, Hobsbawm leaves us with his predictions for the next century, as challenging as the historical analysis presented to the reader in the three preceding volumes. It is hard to praise Hobsbawm too highly - his phenomenal knowledge never stands in the way of his ability to make his books hugely, addictively readable, enjoyable and rewarding.

Hobsbawm, Eric
Nations and Nationalism Since 1780
Cambridge UP pbk £6.95
0521439612

In their national mythologies most nations envision themselves as sprung from ancient and mighty lineages. In truth, a large majority of the nations we recognise today are the creations of the last two hundred years. As one historian remarked, 'Getting one's history wrong is part of being a nation.' This book, expanded from a series of lectures Hobsbawm gave in the 1980s, is a challenging attempt to assess the changing historical nature and importance of nations and nationalism.

Joll, James
Europe Since 1870
Penguin pbk £8.99
0140138439

This has long been one of the major texts on the period for A Level and undergraduate study. It provides a lucid account, allowing the reader to discern the era's main political movements (liberalism, imperialism, fascism, communism) and to trace, within a broader context of economics and demography, their development as they interact. Joll is interested in the idea of Europe as an historical entity. The histories of the various nation-states are considered in the wider framework of the larger whole and the result is a genuinely international history.

Kiernan, Victor
The Lords of Human Kind
Serif pbk £14.99
1897959230

Subtitled *European Attitudes to Other Cultures in the Imperial Age*, Kiernan's book is a massively erudite and entertaining survey of the responses of Europeans to the peoples with whom they came into contact as trade routes were opened up and colonies established. Using a variety of sources - memoirs of explorers and missionaries, the letters of those despatched by the imperial powers to govern newly conquered territories, creative work by writers as diverse as Voltaire and Kipling-Kiernan draws out the range of opinions, occasionally admiring but more often condescending or contemptuous, which Europeans held about non-Europeans.

Lee, Stephen J.
Aspects of European History 1789 -1980
Routledge pbk £10.99
041503468X

Following the pattern of his previous book on earlier centuries, Lee charts the most frequently encountered topics of nineteenth and twentieth century history in a format designed to offer the A-Level student and undergraduate both a broad survey of the period and an introduction to specific historical issues and debates. The structure of the book is intended both to stimulate the student's powers of critical thinking and to assist in the preparation of essays and the undertaking of revision.

McEvedy
Atlas of Recent History Since 1815
Penguin pbk £6.99
014 0511547

Using his well-tried formula of clear and simple maps combined with a succinct explanatory text, McEvedy illuminates the major historical issues in the years since Waterloo.

Rude, George
The Crowd in History
Serif pbk £12.99
18979359214

Subtitled *A Study of Popular Disturbances in France and England 1730-1848*, this is a classic work of what has been called 'history from below', the attempt to see complex historical events through the eyes of the ordinary people involved in them. Rude was one of the first historians to ask certain questions about popular unrest in the late eighteenth and early nineteenth centuries. What sort of people actually stormed the Bastille on the 14th July 1789? Who took part in the intermittent rioting which characterised eighteenth century London? How did Luddism - the movement of agricultural labourers intent on destroying new machinery - spread from one area of the country to another? His book remains a fresh and innovative work of history, accessible to the general reader just as much as to the student of the period.

Taylor, A.J.P.
From Napoleon to the Second International
Penguin pbk £8.99
0140230866

Taylor was a historian whose acute and often acerbic intelligence worked well within the focusing confines of the essay and this collection of his essays on nineteenth century Europe, some not previously published in book form, includes some of his best writing. He writes with equal insight on Metternich and Macaulay, on Peel and Parnell, on Bismarck and Louis Napoleon in this entertaining and readable volume.

Taylor, A.J.P.
The Struggle for Mastery in Europe
Oxford UP pbk £10.99
0198812701

Taylor was one of the most challenging and controversial historians of the century and his skill as a writer, his wit and his insights into historical development and processes mean that his major books remain popular and widely read. This book begins in 1848, the Year of Revolutions, the year in which the established order in Europe was decisively challenged. Taylor traces the rise of Nationalism, the progressive yet ultimately destructive force that shaped the latter part of the nineteenth century. The establishment of the German Empire, the unification of Italy and the stresses placed on existing sovereign states by the creation of these new nations are closely examined.

Thomson, David
Europe Since Napoleon
Penguin pbk £9.99
0140135618

First published in 1957, this acclaimed history has been used by generations of A-Level students and undergraduates and continues to be one of the most comprehensive accounts available of the period it covers. Thomson wrote in the belief that the pattern of European development since 1789 can only be understood by studying those large scale forces which affected the whole continent from Britain to the Balkans. Thus he avoids the temptation to write a series of histories, country by country, agglomerate them and present it as a history of Europe. Instead he emphasises large trends of population growth, industrialisation, nationalism and the connection between war and revolution in such a way that the development of European civilization unfolds as a continuous whole.

Twentieth Century Europe

Carr, E.H.
The Twenty Years' Crisis
Papermac pbk £10.00
0333644697

Subtitled *An Introduction to the Study of International Relations*, this analysis of the period between the World Wars was a pioneering work in the subject and described by Carr himself as an attempt to navigate uncharted waters. Written on the eve of the Second World War and in the shadow of the events it examines, Carr's book is a major achievement. Over fifty years later its insights remain relevant.

Cohn, Norman
Warrant for Genocide
Serif pbk £13.99
1897959257

The Protocols of the Elders of Zion is one of the most pernicious documents in history. Allegedly proof of a worldwide Jewish conspiracy to supplant Christian civilization with a new world order, presided over by a Jewish cabal, it was widely circulated amongst anti-Semitic groups (and continues to be) and was amongst the favoured reading of Hitler and the Nazis. Cohn's book, exact in its research, traces the history of the dangerous myths embodied in the Protocols and examines

the half-crazed world of religious mystics and Russian secret service agents in which it was concocted. Cohn's book is both a careful historical investigation and a warning of the dangers that exist when reason is set aside.

Dawidowicz, Lucy
The War Against the Jews
Penguin pbk £9.99
0140134638

This sober, precise and overwhelming book gives the reader the essential facts about Hitler's war against the Jewish people. In the first part of the book Dawidowicz presents a coherent account of how it came about that the Nazis succeeded in murdering six million Jews; in the second part she examines the ways Jews throughout Europe responded to the assaults that were made first on their property and livelihood and, finally, on their lives. She concludes with a chilling factual overview, country by country, of the murder of European Jews. This is, as George Steiner wrote, 'a profoundly necessary as well as moving reminder of a truth which other historians have found almost too irrational, too incredible to handle.'

Friedrich, Otto
The Kingdom of Auschwitz
Penguin pbk £5.99
0140252533

Auschwitz has become synonymous with the evil and suffering of the Nazi genocide. As Otto Friedrich writes in this moving and harrowing book, 'The Holocaust still horrifies us not because some Jews were murdered - that happens almost every week in New York City - but because the incredible total of six million murders represents the attempt to kill all Jews : genocide. And Auschwitz represents the Holocaust ....because more people died here than anywhere else.' Friedrich draws upon personal testimonies and the memories of survivors to describe the brutalities of life in the camp and the sufferings of those unfortunate enough to be sent there in a book that is an unforgettable reminder of our capacity for evil.

Gilbert, Martin
The Holocaust
Fontana pbk £9.99
0006371949

In his preface to this overwhelmingly painful but necessary book, Gilbert describes his visit to Treblinka in 1959. 'I stepped down from the cart on to the sandy soil : a soil that was grey rather than brown. Driven by I know not what impulse, I ran my hand through that soil again and again. The earth beneath my feet was coarse and sharp: filled with the fragments of human bone.' His history of the Jews during the Second World War is an account of the systematic attempt to destroy European Jewry which led to Treblinka and many other sites in Europe becoming the repositories of unidentified human bones. It also draws upon the testimony of the witnesses closest to the destruction, creating a memorial to the millions who died and whose voices are silent.

Palmer, Alan
Dictionary of Twentieth Century History
Penguin pbk £7.99
0140512640

This dictionary is an essential reference guide to the political, diplomatic, military, social, economic and religious affairs of the present century and a reliable guide to the events and personalities that have shaped the modern world. Palmer has made the dictionary global in its scope and emphasis is placed on events world-wide rather than just in Europe and America. His well-written analyses in each entry convey more than the bare facts and do so in a lucid and concise fashion.

Payne, Stanley G.
History of Fascism 1914-1945
UCL Press pbk £14.95
1857285956

This recent study of fascism in interwar Europe traces its origins to the cultural transformations and anxieties of the *fin de siècle*. Payne then examines the ways in which the catastrophe of the First World War meant the collapse of old social controls and the creation of circumstances in which fascist movements could spring up all over the continent. His book, unsurprisingly, concentrates its investigation on Mussolini's Italy and Nazi Germany but he devotes space to all the major fascist movements in other European countries, particularly Franco's Falangists and the Iron Guards of Romania. This is the most up-to-date and comprehensive survey of the ideology that, tragically, dominated several decades of the century.

Taylor, A.J.P.
The First World War
Penguin pbk £7.99
0140024816

'The unknown soldier was the hero of World War One. He has vanished, except as a cipher, from the written records. He lives again in the photographs.' Thus Taylor describes the importance of photographs as historical evidence in the reconstruction of the experience of men in the Great War and, in this richly illustrated book, he accompanies photographs with his own incisive text. The result is a moving insight into the madness, mutinies and massacres of one of the most terrible wars in history.

Taylor, A.J.P.
The Origins of the Second World War
Penguin pbk £7.99
014013672X

First published in 1961, this work was immediately controversial because its discussion of the years and months preceding the German invasion of Poland on the 1st September 1939 was sceptical of accepted wisdom. Those who glibly blamed Hitler for everything accused Taylor of whitewashing the German dictator and those who had turned Munich into a byword for weakness were upset by his objective treatment - if not defence - of that settlement. More than thirty years on the book remains a provocative and compelling read.

Taylor, A. J.P.
From the Boer War to the Cold War
Penguin pbk £8.99
0140230874

Taylor has been described as 'the most original and incisive historian of his generation' and this collection of essays and reviews provides ample evidence to support this assessment. Whether providing character sketches of politicians as diverse as Joseph Chamberlain and Lloyd George or outlining his groundbreaking ideas about the origins of the two world wars, Taylor demonstrates his rare capacity to address, with wit and style, both his fellow historians and the general reader.

Townson, Duncan
New Penguin Dictionary of Modern History
Penguin pbk £7.99
0140512748

This substantial dictionary, nearly a thousand pages long, is the most useful reference work available in paperback to modern history between the outbreak of the French Revolution and the end of the Second World War. Townson gives extensive coverage to events and people not only in Europe but in the non-European world as well and to the social, political, economic and ideological developments that shaped world history in these years.

Tuchman, Barbara
August 1914
Macmillan pbk £15.00
0333305167

Barbara Tuchman was one of America's most accomplished popular historians and she wrote on a wide variety of subjects from the calamitous fourteenth century in Europe to the first stirrings of the American revolution in the eighteenth century. This epic narrative is her account of the first month of the First World War, thirty days in which, Tuchman argues, the future course of the war was largely determined. She studies in painstaking detail the descent into war and the bloody catalogue of battles in August 1914.

Reproduced from *The Oxford Illustrated History of Modern Europe* (Oxford).

French History

Beevor, Anthony & Cooper, Artemis
Paris After the Liberation
Penguin pbk £8.99
0140230599

This is an excellent evocation of Paris in the aftermath of its liberation from German occupation in 1944, a social and cultural history of a city in which the spirit of joy and freedom and the spirit of revenge were both present. While foreigners arrived to rediscover the pleasures of the newly liberated city, many Parisians themselves had scores to settle and an often rough justice was meted out to those who were seen as erstwhile collaborators with the Nazi regime. Beevor and Cooper have drawn together material from published and unpublished sources, and have interviewed many people who lived in the city at the time, to produce a potent snapshot of Paris at one of the most significant moments in its history.

Briggs, Robin
Early Modern France
Oxford UP pbk £8.99
0192890409

Described by one reviewer as a 'very fine, thorough and conscientious study....one of the best things of its kind in English', Briggs's account of France in the period between 1560 and the death of Louis XIV in 1715 is a well-written introduction to its subject. France in the period witnessed the dramatic events of the Wars of Religion, the Ministry of Richelieu and, of course, the long reign of Le Roi Soleil. Briggs provides the reader with the background necessary to understand and interpret them.

Briggs, Robin
Witches and Neighbours
Fontana pbk £8.99
0006862098

Briggs bases his researches on the French archives in Lorraine but he has used his research and the detailed records of witchcraft trials to re-examine the history of European witchcraft and to see beyond the persecutions to the society which spawned them. David Underdown has written that, 'Briggs is wonderfully alive to the puzzles and complexities that surround the persecutions and convincingly argues that no single cause explanation will work,' and the book represents a new perspective on a perennially fascinating subject.

Bruce, Evangeline
Napoleon and Josephine
Phoenix pbk £9.99
1857994892

Evangeline Bruce subtitles her book *An Improbable Marriage* and her account makes clear how unlikely was the union, begun in the heady atmosphere of post-Terror Paris, between the debt-ridden widow in search of a wealthy protector and the fiercely ambitious young army officer. She traces the course of their often precarious marriage, unsettled by infidelities on both sides and, after Napoleon's astonishingly swift rise to imperial power, by Josephine's inability to produce an heir. Her book is a vivid portrait of the relationship between two remarkable individuals and of the period in which they lived, a period over which they exercised such power and influence.

Burke, Edmund
Reflections on the Revolution in France
Penguin pbk £5.99
0140432043

Burke (1729 -1797) was an Irishman who became a leading figure in both the literary and political worlds of eighteenth century London. He was one of

Revolution such as Lafayette, Mirabeau, Danton and Robespierre and his descriptive set-pieces, often wilfully eccentric, nonetheless retain great power and impact.

Cobb, Richard
The People's Armies
Yale UP pbk £14.95
0300040423

Cobb, author of several volumes of idiosyncratic and highly acclaimed autobiography, was one of the most highly regarded historians of the French Revolution and this book was, perhaps, his major work. The People's Armies were revolutionary civilian groups created to obtain food and equipment from rural areas for the French army. The interaction of the largely urban and highly politicised *armées* with rural villagers was, as Cobb's careful researches make clear, one of the most revealing aspects of the social history of the Revolution.

the greatest of Parliamentary orators and spoke out strongly and frequently against the repression of the American colonies, the conduct of the British in India and in Ireland and the iniquities of the slave trade. His *Reflections on the Revolution in France* was published in 1790 and attacked the revolutionary doctrines being espoused in this country as dangerous abstractions, necessarily producing violence and disorder if put into practice. His treatise provoked spirited responses from many authors, most notably Thomas Paine who wrote *The Rights of Man* as a refutation of Burke's views.

Carlyle, Thomas
The French Revolution
Oxford UP pbk £8.99
0192818430

Carlyle (1795 -1881) was as idiosyncratic an historian as he was a social philosopher and visionary yet his most famous historical work remains readable, an epic narrative of the period from the death of Louis XV to Bonaparte's emergence from Corsican obscurity. His portraits of the great figures of the

Cobban, Alfred
A History of Modern France Volume 1. 1715-1799
Penguin pbk £7.99
0140138250

A History of Modern France Volume 2. 1799-1871
Penguin pbk £7.99
0140138269

A History of Modern France Volume 3. 1871-1962
Penguin pbk £7.99
0140138277

Since its first publication in the sixties, this three-volume history of France from the accession of Louis XV to the time of De Gaulle has established itself, particularly in schools and universities, as an indispensable introduction to its subject. Its particular strength lies in the lucid manner in which Cobban presents the great turning points in French history - 1789, 1848 and the rise of Louis Napoleon, for example - and his skill in weaving an analysis of both the nature of the large historical trends and the motives of the individuals caught up in them into a continuous narrative.

Reproduced from *The Oxford Illustrated History of Modern Europe* (Oxford).

Cronin, Vincent
Napoleon
Fontana pbk £9.99
0006375219

The astonishing trajectory of Napoleon's career, from his Corsican beginnings, through the succession of military triumphs and political manoeuvres that brought him an imperial throne, to the disasters of the Russian campaign and his ultimate defeat at Waterloo and exile and death on St. Helena, has been the subject of countless biographies. This volume by the distinguished historian Vincent Cronin, author of a number of books on the great figures of French history, received much acclaim on its first publication and has continued to hold its place as one of the finest biographies available, particularly accessible to the general reader.

Darnton, Robert
Forbidden Bestsellers
of Pre-Revolutionary France
Fontana pbk £8.99
0006386970

This new book by Robert Darnton, author of the superb collection of essays on eighteenth century French culture and society *The Great Cat Massacre*, derives from what might seem a straightforward yet relatively inconsequential question. What did the French read in the years leading up to the French Revolution? Of course, some read the great *philosophes* of the Enlightenment - Voltaire and Montesquieu, Diderot and Rousseau. Many more read the salacious and blasphemous, often pornograhic books which were sold 'under the cloak' and which were the real bestsellers of the period. Darnton's history of these books and the booksellers involved in selling them is fascinating in its detail and arresting in its suggestion that this literature, so challenging to the orthodox values of the *ancien régime*, may have been as important as the more high-minded writing of the philosophers in preparing the ground for the wholesale rejection of those values that took place in the Revolution.

Davis, Natalie Zemon
The Return of Martin Guerre
Harvard UP pbk £6.95
0674766911

Filmed with Gerard Depardieu in the title role, the basis for a West End musical the story of Martin Guerre seems to carry some particular and powerful resonance for many different audiences. The story is a simple one. In 16th century France a wealthy peasant named Martin Guerre disappears and is not heard from for years. Then he returns - seemingly - to his family and he and his wife enjoy several years of continued marital bliss before the wife suddenly denounces him as an impostor and brings him to trial. The self-styled Martin Guerre is on the verge of winning the case when, at the last moment, the true Martin Guerre reappears. Davis' account of the case and what it tells us about life, love, justice and identity in the period is readable, scholarly and a fascinating work of 'microhistory'.

Reproduced from William Doyle - *The Oxford Illustrated History of the French Revolution* (Oxford).

The French Revolution

Book-length bibliographies of the French Revolution have been published. All that a short essay can do is point to a handful of the titles available beyond those reviewed in our section on French history. Jules Michelet (1794-1874) was one of the greatest of French nineteenth-century historians. His work *La Révolution Francaise* was published in seven volumes between 1847 and 1853, a period when republican hopes were raised and then dashed by the eventual triumph of Louis Napoleon. His history, with its imaginative insights and its democratic fervour, is given its own historical importance by the times and circumstances in which it was written. The University of Chicago publish an edited version of Michelet's epic work, **History of the French Revolution** (0226523330 £13.50), which is worth reading both as narrative and as a window on the view of the Revolution held by a particularly gifted nineteenth century interpreter of it.

Several twentieth century French historians have works on the Revolution in print in this country. Albert Soboul was a leading left-wing historian who died in 1982. His **A Short History of the French Revolution** (University of California P. 0520034198 £9.95) is a valuable precis of his work and **The Sans-Culottes** (Princeton UP 0691007829 £14.50) is a study of the relationship between popular movements and the revolutionary government in 1793-94. Francois Furet's **The French Revolution 1770-1814** (Blackwell 0631202994 £11.99), which is the first volume of a longer examination of France's revolutionary inheritance, offers a re-interpretation of events from the Fall of the Bastille to the eve of Napoleon's defeat. Michel Vovelle's book **The Fall of the French Monarchy** (0521289165 £14.95), which covers the years immediately before and after 1789, is one of a sequence of titles published in translation by Cambridge University Press. Sadly the others in this sequence, including a useful book by Marc Bouloiseau on the Jacobin rule, are currently unavailable. Two one-volume works by historians writing in English, other than those reviewed separately, are worth consulting. Jeremy Popkin's **A Short History of the French Revolution** (Prentice-Hall 0132884240 £12.50) is a concise overview of the major events and the different ways historians have interpreted them. **The French Revolution** (Blackwell 0631119213 £14.99) by J.M. Thompson is a substantial work by a historian who has also written a valuable life of Robespierre, unfortunately now out of print.

The origins of the Revolution have been much debated. William Doyle's **Origins of the French Revolution** (Oxford UP 019822284X £9.99) is a concise introduction to that debate. **The Genesis of the French Revolution** (Cambridge UP 0521445701 £12.95), edited by Bailey Stone, is an original examination of the causes of the Revolution which tries to set France and its revolution within an international setting. **Inventing the French Revolution** (Cambridge UP 0521385784 £17.95), edited by Keith Baker, is a collection of essays on its ideological origins and the political culture from which it sprang. Other books, which have a particular perspective on the Revolution, include Norman Hampson's **A Social History of the French Revolution** (Routledge 0415119529 £13.99). Hampson is the author of biographies of Danton and Saint-Just but, in this volume, he analyses the nature of the social conflicts within French society which fuelled the Revolution. **The Peasantry in the French Revolution** (Cambridge UP 052133716X £14.95), by P.M. Jones, usefully fills a gap in the literature on the Revolution. **Britain and the French Revolution** (Macmillan 033344261X £13.50) investigates the impact in this country of events across the Channel and the varying responses to them. **Blood Sisters** (Pandora Press 0044409184 £12.99) is an interesting collection of writings by women who witnessed the upheavals of the times. Mona Ozouf's book **Festivals and the French Revolution** (Harvard UP 0674298845 £12.95) is an original analysis of revolutionary festivals which looks to find answers to the question of why revolutionaries of all stripes seemed obseessed with public celebration.

The French Revolution in Social and Political Perspective (Arnold 034065290X £15.99), edited by Peter Jones, is a useful and recently published reader which examines the sort of debates in which contemporary historiansof the Revolution are engaged. **The Longman Companion to the French Revolution** (Longman 0582494176 £24.00) is a compendium of information - revolutionary terms, brief biographies of more than 500 revolutionary figures - which is an excellent reference tool. Two books which, in different ways, investigate not only the major events of the Revolution but also the approaches of historians to those events are **The French Revolution:Rethinking the Debate** (Routledge 0415154664 £6.99), edited by Gwynne Lewis, and the far more substantial **The Rise and Fall of the French Revolution** (University of Chicago Press 0226056929 £17.95), edited by T.C.W. Blanning, which offers the reader a measured combination of narrative and interpretation. Florin Aftalion's book **The French Revolution: An Economic Interpretation** (Cambridge UP 0521368103 £12.95) is a re-examination of accepted beliefs that economic factors were peripheral to the essentially political nature of the Revolution.

Finally, if some of these titles appear a little heavyweight or over-academic, there is always **The French Revolution for Beginners** (Writers and Readers 086316014X £8.95), by Martin McCrory, one of a series of titles which explain the ideas and events of past and present in easily digestible form, accompanied by cartoons and caricatures.

Joan of Arc in 1431. Duby focuses on the gradual emergence of a recognisable French state from competing centres of power in a book that is both scholarly and readable.

Doyle, William
Oxford History of the French Revolution
Oxford UP pbk £8.99
0192852213

Many books on the subject were published to coincide with the bicentenary of the outbreak of the French Revolution and many went rapidly out of print but this comprehensive survey, drawing on a wealth of research and scholarly debate, is likely to remain the standard textbook for many years to come. It is also an accessible narrative which carries the reader from the crisis of Louis XVI's government in the 1780s, through the storming of the Bastille, the descent into terror, the events of Thermidor, to the government of the Directory and the transformation of the revolution into Napoleon's imperial rule.

Duby, Georges
France in the Middle Ages
Blackwell pbk £15.99
0631189459

Georges Duby is a major French historian and this volume in the Blackwell History of France series is a significant reinterpretation of the formative period in French history between the rise of the Capetians in the mid-tenth century and the execution of

Hibbert, Christopher
The French Revolution
Penguin pbk £8.99
0140049452

Hibbert's characteristically lucid narrative provides a reliable introduction to the Revolution for the general reader, covering the ten years from the meeting of the Estates General in 1789 to the *coup d'état* of 18 Brumaire which brought Napoleon to power. His emphasis is firmly on events and people rather than ideas and the narrative is divided into a number of chapters which recount the actions of the particular *journées* which shaped the course of the Revolution - the Day of the Tennis Court Oath, the Day of the Vainqueurs de la Bastille, the Days of the Tuileries, the Days of the September Massacres, the Days of the Terror and others. Hibbert's almost exclusive concentration on events in Paris does limit the picture of the Revolution that he presents but his skills as a popular historian are evident throughout the book.

Horne, Alistair
The Fall of Paris
Macmillan pbk £9.99
0333499514

In the aftermath of the humiliating defeat inflicted by the Prussians on the French at Sedan in 1870, further anguish

followed for the inhabitants of the French capital. Paris was besieged for many months and many citizens reduced to desperate measures to stay alive. The last resistance came from the revolutionary Communards in May 1871 but they were ruthlessly suppressed by government troops from outside the city, in dreadful scenes which saw Frenchman killing Frenchman by the thousand. Alistair Horne's vivid account of these events is the first in a loosely connected trio of books about the conflict between France and Germany over seventy years.

Horne, Alistair
How Far From Austerlitz
Macmillan hbk £20.00
0333655494

Austerlitz, Napoleon's brilliant victory in 1805 over a larger force of Austrian and Russian troops, was, seen in retrospect, as the pinnacle of his success. Ironically this greatest of his victories was also the beginning of the ten year process which led to Waterloo. The sheer magnitude of his success on the field of Austerlitz led Napoleon into the delusional belief that no force or combination of forces was able to prevent him achieving his desires for greater conquest. Further victories were, of course, to follow but the over-reaching ambition that led him into the catastrophic Russian campaign of 1812 began to beckon. Alistair Horne has written another vivid story of French military drama in this account of the ten years which took Napoleon from his apogee at Austerlitz to his downfall at Waterloo.

Horne, Alistair
A Savage War of Peace
Papermac pbk £15.00
0333669517

The Algerian War of 1954-1962 was one of the most dramatic and bloody conflicts in the transition between imperialism and a post-colonial world. An estimated one million Muslim Algerians were killed and as many European settlers were expelled from their homes. The war was the direct cause of the fall of half a dozen French Prime Ministers and contributed significantly to the collapse of the Fourth French Republic. De Gaulle's Fifth Republic was threatened and there were at least two occasions when France itself teetered on the verge of civil war because of the wider repercussions of the conflict. Alistair Horne has written what is the best volume available in English on the drama, both heroic and tragic, that is known in France as *la guerre d'Algerie* and in Algeria as the Revolution.

Knecht, R.J.
The Rise and Fall of Renaissance France
Fontana pbk £9.99
0006861679

The sixteenth century in France was a century of religious and political upheaval, of almost ceaseless strife and battle which saw the country's fortunes ebb both literally and metaphorically. It was also a century which saw some of the greatest art and thought of the Renaissance emerge from France. The years which witnessed the massacre of St. Bartholomew and civil war between Catholic and Huguenot were also the years in which Montaigne wrote his essays and Rabelais was read and enjoyed. Knecht's account of this colourful and confusing period in French history is both an authoritative narrative of the century's events and a stimulating analysis of the cultural, economic and social contexts in which they took place.

Ladurie, Emmanuel Le Roy
Montaillou
Penguin pbk £9.99
0140137009

The Cathar heresy, or Albigensianism, appeared to have been stamped out by the ruthlessness of the Albigensian crusade in the early 13th century and to have disappeared with the taking of the last Cathar stronghold at Montségur in 1244. However, adherents of the faith continued to exist in remote villages in South West France such as Montaillou, as is revealed in the documents and testimony surviving from a renewed inquisition into the heresy, undertaken in the early fourteenth century. From these documents Ladurie has built up an extraordinary portrait of the life and inhabitants of a medieval village, perhaps the most detailed ever created. As Richard Cobb wrote in a review of the book when it was first published, 'It is so good, so human that, as at the end of a great novel, one is sorry to leave the endearing company of the Clergue brothers, of the smiling Pierre Maury, of the generous Béatrice, the saintly Authié brothers, the rascally Bélibaste, and the young girls and old women with the extraordinary names.'

Lefebvre, Georges
The Coming of the French Revolution
Princeton UP pbk £7.95
0691007519

Lefebvre (1874-1959) was one of the most distinguished French historians of his generation, a pioneer of 'history from below' and a longtime colleague of Marc Bloch, one of the founders of the hugely influential journal *Annales*. First published in 1939, his analysis of the events leading up to the French Revolution is heavily influenced by Marxist thinking, an influence clear in the way he uses class to subdivide neatly the causes of the Revolution. His approach has seemed unnecessarily constricting to many later historians but his work remains lucid and readable, possessed of a dramatic sense of the gathering impetus of the Revolution.

Price, Roger
Concise History of France
Cambridge UP pbk £9.95
052136809X

This is succinct and clear account of French history from the emergence of a strong state centred on the Île de France in the early middle ages through to the Mitterand presidency. Price considers the relationship between state and society, the impact of long periods of warfare and examines questions of political power through these centuries - who possessed it, how they used it and to what effect. The great figures of French history - Philip Augustus, Henri IV, Louis XIV and the two Napoleons - are central to his text but he also incorporates the researches of recent social historians into the lives, deaths and beliefs of ordinary people.

Rude, George
The French Revolution
Phoenix pbk £9.99
1857991265

One of the clearest one-volume accounts of the Revolution, Rude's book explains how the events of this turning point in European history mark the downfall of the *ancien régime*, the rise of democracy and the emergence of the working class as a recognisable political force. Rude covers all the major incidents of the period from the storming of the Bastille to the coming of Napoleon, including the political struggles on the streets, of which he has written so well in other books, and investigates the motives of those who participated in them. In his conclusion he looks closely at the wider implications the Revolution carried, and still carries, in the history of Europe and describes some of the historiographical debate that has raged over its significance.

Schama, Simon
Citizens
Penguin pbk £20.00
0140172068

At the heart of Schama's history of the French Revolution is the transformation in the way individuals viewed themselves, and were viewed by people in power, that permanently affected the course of European history, the transformation of 'subjects' into 'citizens'. The author of *The Embarrassment of Riches* and *Landscape and Memory* shows the reader a France in the midst of dramatic social and economic change, seized by a euphoric vision of liberty. He draws on all the riches of cultural, social and political history for this account of how the great upheaval soon became a source of terror and death, changing France forever. This is a magnificent and compelling narrative history as well as what Eric Hobsbawm described as 'a passionate manifesto against violence.'

Williams, Gwyn A.
Artisans and Sans-Culottes
Libris pbk £.11.95
1870352807

First published in 1968, itself a revolutionary year in many ways, Williams' book is the only concise account available of those radical popular movements which sprang up in France, and in Britain, during the French Revolution. The new edition of what Richard Cobb called 'a first-rate human history' was published twenty years later and includes a substantial new introduction which has more to say about the role of women in these movements and about activities outside the great cities.

German History

Bessel, Richard
Life in the Third Reich
Oxford UP pbk £8.99
0192851845
This collection of essays by eight historians, including Detlev Peukert and Ian Kershaw, throws fresh light on familiar topics such as the role of political violence in the Nazi rise to power and illuminates some less familiar ones such as the nature of village life in the Third Reich. It is a fine instance of that recent scholarly work on Hitler's Germany which has sought to look beyond the narrative of political events to examine the structure of the society behind the propaganda.

Blackbourn, David
Fontana History of Germany 1815 -1918
HarperCollins hbk £27.50
0002556774
In the late eighteenth century German-speaking Europe was a patchwork of tiny principalities, hundreds in total, in which the majority of the people lived a rural, peasant existence. One hundred years later Germany was united under the rule of Bismarck's Prussia and was an industrial and military giant which ranked as one of the great world powers. Blackbourn's account of this transformation -

how politically Germany came to be unified, how social relations within the unified nation had developed and what the cultural consequences were - is a significant new addition to the required reading list for anyone interested in modern German history.

Bullock, Alan
Hitler : A Study in Tyranny
Penguin pbk £9.99
0140135642
First published in 1952, and subsequently revised in 1962, after the increasing number of available documents justified a re-examination of some ideas in the first edition, this book continues to be regarded as a major source on the subject. The book is very much about Hitler himself. Bullock's avowed intent was to try and establish how much the Third Reich was intimately tied up with the personal power and charisma of one individual. His book is acknowledged as a great and powerful biographical portrait; that it is also one of the most balanced and objective histories of the Third Reich is testament both to Bullock's considered and objective study of archive material, and to the increasingly indivisible relationship between Hitler and his political and military machine.

Bullock, Alan
Hitler and Stalin : Parallel Lives
HarperCollins pbk £12.99
0006861989
Alan Bullock is the author of a biography of Hitler, first published in the fifties, but still regarded as definitive and authoritative. Hitler and Stalin never met but this superb parallel history interweaves their lives into the tapestry of twentieth century events to create a joint portrait, compelling in its detail, of the century's greatest dictators. Bullock alternates chapters on the Nazi and Soviet leaders, showing how and why their careers developed, what motivated them, how they were alike and how they differed. The book is both an appraisal of two severely damaged characters whose beliefs and actions had such terrible consequences and a sweeping account of the crucial formative years of this century.

Craig, Gordon A.
Germany 1866 -1945
Oxford UP pbk £11.99
0192851012
The German Empire, of which Bismarck was the founding spirit, pursued expansionist policies which led it into unavoidable competition with the other great powers and it disintegrated in

Fulbrook, Mary
Concise History of Germany
Cambridge UP pbk £9.95
0521368367

the anarchic aftermath of the First World War. The Weimar Republic was its short-lived successor, doomed by economic woes and the inability of its politicians to deal with the rising threat of Fascism. Hitler's Third Reich was a descent into national madness and the worst chapter in German history. Craig's book which was described in the Sunday Times on first publication as 'the best one-volume work on modern Germany' is a study of the main political, social and cultural events of this period and of the individuals who shaped, and were shaped by, them.

Reproduced from *The Oxford Illustrated History of Modern Europe* (Oxford).

Cambridge University Press publish an admirable series of concise histories of different nations which are written by major scholars with a general readership in mind. Mary Fulbrook's contribution to the series tackles the multi-faceted, problematic history of the German lands, which has provoked a wide range of debates and differences of interpretation. She provides a crisp synthesis of a vast array of material and explores the interrelationship between social, political and cultural factors in the light of scholarly controversies.

Fulbrook, Mary
Fontana History of Germany 1918-1990
Fontana pbk £8.99
0006861113

Division has been at the heart of German history since 1918 - from the weakness and instability of the Weimar Republic through the extremes of the Nazi period to the political separation of the nation in the post-war years. In the forty years after the war the two Germanies appeared to have created successful solutions to the problems of German history but they too were based on shifting ground, as the sudden collapse of the wall and the difficult consequences of a swift transition to a unified country have proved. Mary Fulbrook's book is

a powerful new interpretation of modern German history viewed from the perspective of reunification.

Gill, Anton
A Dance Between Flames
Abacus pbk £7.99
0349106290

Focusing on Berlin at a time between the two world wars when it was one of the most vibrant and radical cities in the world, Gill's book chronicles the cultural upheavals of the Weimar period, the rich experimentation in art and literature, music and architecture, and the turbulent society in which the rise of Nazism took place. He moves on to assess the city under Nazi rule, the persecution of its Jewish population, the exercise in racial self-promotion that was the 1936 Olympic Games and Hitler's unfulfilled dreams for a megalomaniac rebuilding of the city. He concludes with the sombre ironies of the destruction of so much of Berlin by allied bombing.

Jonathan Miller has called an 'unbearably painful book which forces one to fundamentally reappraise the events of the Second World War'.

Goldhagen, Daniel
Hitler's Willing Executioners
Abacus pbk £9.99
0349107866

Goldhagen's book has been a controversial bestseller in a number of countries and, unsurprisingly, has created a huge furore in Germany. His thesis is implied by the book's subtitle, *Ordinary Germans and the Holocaust*. Goldhagen argues that many beliefs about the perpetrators of the atrocities of the Holocaust and the motives for their brutalities are fallacies. They were not primarily SS men or fanatical Nazis but ordinary Germans from all walks of life. They carried out their deeds not because of irresistible coercion, not because they slavishly followed orders, not because of peer pressure. They murdered and tormented Jews because of a widespread and virulent antisemitism which led them to believe that the Jews were less than human, an enemy whose extermination was morally justifiable. Goldhagen skilfully marshals a huge array of evidence to support his thesis in what

Grunberger, Richard
A Social History of the Third Reich
Penguin pbk £11.00
0140136754

Most of the multitude of books written on Hitler's Reich concentrate on the political and military history of those terrible twelve years. Yet, amidst the violence and persecution, the war and devastation, ordinary Germans continued to lead everyday lives, although those everyday lives were shaped by Nazi propaganda and the cult of the Führer. Drawing on contemporary sources - memoirs, letters, newspapers - Grunberger has produced a massive reconstruction of 'ordinary' life under the Nazi regime. What films did people watch? What political jokes did they tell? How did they view the family and the role of women in society? These are just a few of the questions to which Grunberger's book provides answers.

Mann, Golo
History of Germany Since 1789
Pimlico pbk £12.50
0712674403

This major work of history by Golo Mann, the son of the novelist and Nobel prizewinner Thomas Mann, was first translated into English in 1968. 'At times', Mann wrote, 'the Germans seem a philosophical

people, at others the most practical and materialistic, at times the most patient and peaceful, at others the most domineering and brutal.' It is on this notion of paradox that Mann's sensitive narrative pivots. He traces the whole sweep of German history in the period since the French Revolution, chronicling historical events and dealing in detail with the contributions of philosophers, poets and novelists alongside those of parliamentarians and generals.

Nicholls, A.J.
Weimar and the Rise of Hitler
Macmillan pbk £12.50
0333550994

One of a series which examines in detail important and controversial events and themes in twentieth century history, this is a study of the failure of the Weimar Republic and the concomitant rise of the Nazi party, culminating in the selection of Hitler as Chancellor in January 1933. Nicholls looks at the factors which contributed to the Republic's failure in the context of its entire fifteen-year existence, from its emergence after defeat and revolution had rocked Germany in 1918, through its frequent economic and social crises, to its eventual demise.

Peukert, Detlev
The Weimar Republic
Penguin pbk £7.99
0140125795

The Weimar Republic was born from Germany's defeat in the First World War and came to an end amidst the paralysis of the anti-fascist forces that enabled Hitler to come to power in January 1933. Peukert's book is an account of the fifteen years in which the republic staggered from crisis to crisis, its politicians striving to deal with an already tottering economy faced by a world-wide depression and a society in which traditional class structures had been broken down. He analyses the failures of the welfare schemes established by the republic, looks at the changing social relationships between the generations and between the sexes, and charts the flourishing of mass culture in what is a comprehensive and authoritative study of its subject.

Sereny, Gitta
Albert Speer: His Battle with Truth
Picador pbk £7.99
0330346970

This biography of Speer, the architect and intellectual who became Minister for Armaments in the Third Reich and one of the leading figures in the Nazi High Command, is one of the most significant books to have appeared on the Nazi period in recent years. Speer was the only leading Nazi at the Nuremberg trials to acknowledge any responsibility for the crimes of the regime which he served. Yet his acknowledgement of guilt remained equivocal. Exactly how much did Speer know about the fate of the Jews in Germany and Eastern Europe and how thoroughly did he face up to his guilt? Gitta Sereny has sifted through documentary evidence, spent many years interviewing witnesses and conducted a series of conversations with Speer himself, who died in 1981, established firmly in the role of the Nazi who accepted responsibility. She has written an epic but subtly nuanced biography of a gifted and complex man and she allows the reader to come to his or her own interpretation of Speer's claim that 'It is possible to live in a twilight between knowing and not knowing.'

Shirer, William
The Rise and Fall of the Third Reich
Mandarin pbk £12.99
0749306971

This remains one of the classic accounts of the Third Reich.

Shirer was present at the Nuremberg trials of the surviving Nazi leaders and had full access to the German archives. His massive book covers the early days of the Nazi party in Bavaria, its rise in popularity during the twenties, its path to power through streetfighting and the ballot box, the persecution of the Jews, the drift to war, the sickening horrors of the final solution and Hitler's last, demented days in the bunker. Shirer was a journalist rather than a professional historian and his work has the virtues of the best reporting in its readability and attention to detail.

Reproduced from *The Oxford Illustrated History of Modern Europe* (Oxford).

Speer, Albert
Inside the Third Reich
Phoenix pbk £9.95
1857992180

Speer, recently the subject of a much acclaimed biography by Gitta Sereny, was Hitler's favourite architect, entrusted with the opportunity to transform Berlin into a suitably grandiose capital for the Reich. During the war he was made Minister of Armaments and, at the Nuremberg trials, he was the only Nazi of any standing to admit any kind of responsibility for the actions of the regime. He served twenty years in Spandau prison and published these memoirs after his release. They remain indispensable reading on the period, whether viewed as a fascinating insider's view of Hitler and the Third Reich or, as some critics have claimed, a monumental and subtle exercise in self-justification.

Trevor-Roper, Hugh
The Last Days of Hitler
Macmillan pbk £10.00
0333642619

In the months after the war came to an end the circumstances surrounding Hitler's death or disappearance remained mysterious. Despite the broadcast statement by Admiral Doenitz that Hitler had died fighting with his troops in Berlin, rumours of his escape, some more plausible than others (he was variously alleged to be in a Spanish monastery, on a South American ranch and holed up with friendly bandits in the mountains of Albania), continued to circulate. Hugh Trevor-Roper, then an intelligence officer with the British Army, was assigned the task of discovering the truth. The result was this book, first published in 1947 and rarely out of print since. It has been described by A.J.P. Taylor as a book for which 'no words of praise are too strong.' Trevor-Roper proved, beyond any reasonable doubt, that Hitler had killed himself in his bunker and gave a compelling picture of the lunatic disintegration of the Nazis' proposed Thousand Year Reich.

Wistrich, Robert
Who's Who in Nazi Germany
Routledge pbk £10.99
0415118883

An indispensable reference work for anyone interested in the Third Reich. The book includes concise biographies not only of the leading politicians and generals of the regime but also industrialists, artists, entertainers and sportsmen who made their mark in the period. In addition there are brief articles on those, like von Stauffenberg and the Scholls, who gave their lives in attempts to resist the tyrannies of the Reich.

Reproduced from *The Oxford Illustrated History of Modern Europe (Oxford)*.

Italian History

Duggan, Christopher
Concise History of Italy
Cambridge UP pbk £9.95
0521408482
This is a short, illustrated account of Italian history from the collapse of the Roman empire in the West to the present day. For most of these centuries Italy was not a nation but, in the well-known remark by Metternich, 'a geographical expression', and Duggan, in this lucid and well-written narrative, focuses particularly on the last two centuries and the difficulties Italy has faced in forging a nation state.

Ginsborg, Paul
History of Contemporary Italy
Penguin pbk £8.99
0140124969
Ginsborg's book is an authoritative analysis of the social and political history of Italy in the period since the fall of Mussolini, a period in which a war-torn, poverty-stricken and largely agrarian country transformed itself into the troubled but resilient society of today. The continuing search for political reform and the rooting out of corruption is chronicled, as is its continual frustration, and the book examines also the declining, but still significant, role of the Catholic church.

Ginzburg, Carlo
The Cheese and the Worms
Penguin pbk £8.99
0140168753
On first publication this book was described as 'one of the most penetrating, elegant and readable contributions yet made to the history of popular culture'. By exploring the life of an Italian miller Menocchio and reconstructing his idiosyncratic, personal cosmology, Ginzburg illuminates the peasant culture of the late sixteenth century. Using the records of the trial, in which Menocchio was accused of heresy and eventually condemned to be burnt at the stake, he recreates brilliantly the materials from which the independent miller built his world-view.

Hibbert, Christopher
Garibaldi and His Enemies
Penguin pbk £8.99
0140079718
Garibaldi was the great, charismatic figure in the struggle for Italian unification and his exploits in the revolutionary years of 1848-9 made him a hero to most nationalists. In 1860 his successful invasion of Sicily with his guerrilla army, the Thousand, his defeat of the King of Naples in two battles and his eventual crossing to the mainland and capture of Naples were, in most ways, the decisive events in the unification of the country under Victor Emmanuel II. Hibbert's vivid account of Garibaldi's tempestuous career as guerrilla general is also a narrative of the events which led to Italy becoming one nation.

Hibbert, Christopher
The Rise and Fall of the House of Medici
Penguin pbk £8.99
0140050906
The Medici amassed great wealth through their banking activities and exerted great political and cultural influence from the 14th century onwards as they lavished it on the building of grand palaces, the commissioning of great works of art and the patronage of writers and poets. Members of the family like Cosimo de Medici and Lorenzo the Magnificent were as important to the flowering of the Florentine Renaissance as any of the artists they employed. Hibbert's book is a readable history of this extraordinary family from the rise of the Medici bank in the late fourteenth century to the death of the last Medici Grand Duke of Tuscany, Gian Gastone, in 1737.

Mack Smith, Denis
Italy and its Monarchy
Yale UP pbk £11.95
0300051328
This study of the four Savoyard
kings who ruled Italy in the
period between unification in
1861 and the foundation of the
republic after the Second World
War is a major work by a leading
and much acclaimed English-
language historian of Italy. Mack
Smith's central argument, that
the monarchy was discredited as
an institution of government
because its willingness to accept
responsibility for political events
was not matched by an ability to
control them, emerges from a text
that is rich in detail and research.

Norwich, John Julius
A History of Venice
Penguin pbk £20.00
0140066233
This one-volume version of a
work originally published in two
volumes is a loving and scholarly
portrayal of the history of one of
the most beautiful cities in the
world. John Julius Norwich
traces the story of Venice from
its earliest beginnings in Dark
Age Italy, through the period of
its greatest commercial and mercantile power, to its long decline
and the final disappearance of
the Republic in 1797. Another
author who is a long-time devotee of Venice, Jan Morris, has
described this book as 'the
standard Venetian history in
English.'

Origo, Iris
The Merchant of Prato
Penguin pbk £9.99
0140172181
Using the surviving letters and
records of the 14th century
Tuscan merchant Francesco
Datini, Iris Origo creates a
remarkable portrait of Italian
domestic and commercial life on
the eve of the Renaissance.
Origo's access to Datini's archive
of 150,000 business and personal
letters is exploited to great effect
in a work that is filled with rich
and intricate details of daily life.

Procacci, Giuliano
History of the Italian People
Penguin pbk £8.99
0140135901
'This book sets out to describe
how, in the course of a long and
varied history, Italy has contributed to the formation and
development of modern
European civilization. Italy's history, in other words, forms part
of Europe's...' Thus writes
Procacci in his introduction and
his account of Italy's often turbulent past, from a starting point
at 1000 A.D., when its cities and
towns were self-governing,
through to the rise and fall of
Fascism this century, is focused
on this wish to set events in Italy
in the wider European context.

Reproduced from *The Oxford Illustrated History of Modern Europe* (Oxford).

Russian and Soviet History

Conquest, Robert
The Great Terror
Pimlico pbk £15.00
0712652531

The original edition of this book was published in 1968. This revised and updated version, appearing in 1990, makes full use of material which has recently become available giving further depth to the account of the purges in Stalin's Russia which, between 1934 and 1939, cost many millions their lives. Conquest gives due attention to the great show trials which culminated in the accusations levelled at, amongst others, Bukharin and two other members of Lenin's Politburo, and he also recounts the suffering in the labour camps of many less exalted victims of Stalin's terror. Harrison Salisbury described the book as, 'Not only an odyssey of madness, tragedy, sadism, but a work of scholarship and literary craftsmanship.'

Deutscher, Isaac
Stalin
Penguin pbk £11.00
0140135049

Deutscher (1907-1967) was born in Poland, joined the Polish communist party in 1926 and was expelled six years later because of his activities as leader and spokesman of the anti-Stalinists in the party. He came to Britain in 1939 where he spent the rest of his career as a journalist, academic and political commentator. His controversial biography of Stalin was first published in 1948 and was substantially updated and revised in the year before Deutscher's death. Although inevitably coloured and shaped by Deutscher's own political career and convictions, the book remains an invaluable work which examines the nature of Stalin's dominance of Soviet society and the extent to which he was or was not the natural successor to Lenin. Deutscher also wrote an epic, three-volume life of Trotsky which is, sadly, out of print.

Figes, Orlando
A People's Tragedy
Cape hbk £20.00
0224041622

In the wake of the collapse of the Soviet empire and the continuing dramas in Russian political life, a new account of the revolutionary era from which the Soviet Union emerged is welcome and Figes's epic narrative, vast in ambition and prodigious in its learning, deserves all the acclaim it has received. Figes argues that the confrontation between the demands of the people and the rigidity of the old autocratic order, which led inevitably to revolution, need not have led inevitably to dictatorship and his story, at least in part, tells how Lenin and the Bolsheviks subverted democratic aspirations in pursuit of their own objectives. His skill in presenting a broad canvas of war, revolution and counter-revolution is matched by his ability to evoke the lives of individuals - the patriotic general Brusilov, the reforming aristocrat Prince Lvov, the often disillusioned socialist writer Gorky and many others - enmeshed in a society in upheaval.

Fitzpatrick, Sheila
The Russian Revolution
Oxford UP pbk £7.95
0192892576

The Russian Revolution has been described as 'the central event of twentieth century history.' This succinct volume is an account not only of the events of 1917 but of the entire process of social transformation undertaken by the Bolsheviks after they had come to power. Fitzpatrick follows the progress of the revolution, from the destruction of tsarism to the ruthless creation of the Stalinist state, and examines the important question of how far Stalin completed the revolution that Lenin had begun and how far he betrayed it. The second edition, recently published, makes use of new documents and archive material only available in the last few years.

Hingley, Ronald
Russia : A Concise History
Thames & Hudson pbk £7.95
0500276277

Russia's problems today and the challenges facing her, in the wake of the dissolution of the Soviet Empire, can only be fully understood as the latest act in a long and unfolding drama. This highly illustrated and succinct account of Russian history, from the beginnings as an illiterate pagan community of eastern Slavs, to glasnost and beyond is a clear introduction for the general reader to a vast and complex subject.

Hopkirk, Peter
Setting the East Ablaze
Oxford UP pbk £6.99
0192851667

Hopkirk has a great narrative gift and his accounts of nineteenth and early twentieth century espionage and skulduggery in Central Asia, such as *The Great Game* and *On Secret Service East of Constantinople*, make exciting reading. This book is an equally gripping tale of intrigue in the region, this time the intrigue fostered by Lenin after the Bolshevik revolution in an attempt to foment trouble and uprisings in British India. Once again Hopkirk has thrown light on a fascinating but obscure corner of imperial history.

Hosking, Geoffrey
A History of the Soviet Union
Fontana pbk £9.99
000686287X

Now that the Soviet empire has unravelled and long-hidden territorial conflicts have been renewed, it is even more important than before to understand the vast state bureaucracy that held so many disparate peoples together. How it did so forms the core of this highly praised book, published in a revised edition in 1992. Hosking traces the evolution and downfall of the political system of the world's last great land empire, from its revolutionary beginnings in 1917 to the collapse brought about by perestroika.

Keep, John
Last of the Empires
Oxford UP pbk £9.99
0192892371

In 1945 the Soviet Union had survived the dreadful traumas of the battle against Hitler's Germany to emerge as one of the Allied victors. Stalin was one of the principal architects of the Europe that was to be built from the rubble of the war and his country was in a position of massive power and prestige, its influence and control variously apparent throughout Eastern Europe. In 1991 the Soviet Union was in a state of collapse and disintegration, a superpower in danger of losing all internal stability and much of its influence in the world at large. Keep's readable history of the years between these two dates is particularly successful in tracing the reasons behind the thawing of the Soviet monolith, in examining the pressures pulling its empire apart and in giving a reasoned assessment of the revolution from above which Gorbachev attempted to orchestrate.

Kochan, Lionel
The Making of Modern Russia
Penguin pbk £8.99
0140136487

First published in 1963, this book continues to be an excellent one-volume introduction to Russian history. The title gives little sense of the sheer scope of this survey. The author chooses the sixth century and the settling of the Slavs on the Russian plain as his starting point, and carries the narrative through brief and incisive accounts of the Mongol conquest, the birth of the nation-state and the emergence of the Romanov dynasty, to major chapters on the collapse of tsarist power, the Bolshevik revolution, Stalin's regime and beyond. Few books are so successful at placing the problems and developments of twentieth century Russia in their historical perspective.

Massie, Robert K.
Peter the Great
Abacus pbk £13.99
0349104611

Peter the Great, who came to power in Russia in 1689, was a ruler of enormous contradictions and paradoxes. During his reign the integration of Russia into the West was hastened, largely because of Peter's own enlightened attitudes towards the sciences and industry and because of his willingness to copy more advanced countries. However he was also a man of barbarous cruelty, still rooted, in many ways, in the feudalism of previous generations. Massie's biography won a Pulitzer Prize and is the most detailed and convincing investigation of a complex man who was centrally important to the development of early modern Russia.

Massie, Robert K.
Nicholas and Alexandra
Gollancz pbk £7.99
0575400064

Massie has the gift of investing historical narrative with life and colour and his account of the private and public life of the last of the Romanovs is highly detailed and immensely enjoyable. The material he has to draw upon, of course, is extraordinary and demands the dramatic portrayal that Massie gives it. The weak and vacillating Nicholas, inheritor of a throne for which he was clearly unsuited and which he didn't himself want, and the German-born Alexandra, granddaughter of Queen Victoria, preside over the riches of the Imperial court while the vast majority of their subjects live in poverty. Their only son is haemophiliac and a bizarre monk called Rasputin, half-mystic, half-charlatan, gains exceptional power at court because of his apparent ability to control the effects of the illness. In the First World War a revolution sweeps them from their throne and they are killed at Ekaterinburg in mysterious circumstances which are still debated eighty years later. Massie organises this material into a gripping and intelligent narrative.

Reproduced from *The Oxford Illustrated History of Modern Europe* (Oxford).

Moynahan, Brian
The Russian Century
Pimlico pbk £10.00
0712673091

Brian Moynahan is the former European editor of the Sunday Times and the author of two previous books on Russian history. In this work he has succeeded in compressing the broad sweep of Russian history in the last hundred years, from the last years of the Romanovs, through revolution, Stalinist terror and war with Germany to the era of glasnost and perestroika and the uneasy present, into a succinct and extremely readable narrative. It is the ideal short history for the general reader of this terrible century for the Russian people.

Pipes, Richard
Russia under the Old Regime
Penguin pbk £9.99
0140247688

This authoritative volume covers the period from the 9th century to the late nineteenth century. Part One describes the evolution of the Russian state. Part Two analyses the political behaviour of the principal social groups of the Empire (the peasantry, the nobility, the bourgeoisie and the clergy) and their inability to stem the increasing absolutism of the Tsar. Part Three looks at the intelligentsia's challenge to the regime and the state's response in developing into a bureaucratic police state.

Pipes, Richard
The Russian Revolution
Fontana pbk £16.99
0006862330

This comprehensive and detailed survey of the Russian Revolution embraces not only the political and military struggle for power in the crucial years but the entire movement to revolutionise state and society from 1899 to 1919. Pipes focuses on the decay of Tsarism from the turn of the century, culminating in the mutiny of the Petrograd garrison in February 1917, and goes on to describe the sequence of events in the Bolshevik seizure of power and imposition of one-party rule. Pipes is one of the most respected of all Russian historians in English and he has written what A.N. Wilson described in a review as 'the best book on the Russian Revolution I have ever read.'

Radzinsky, Edvard
Stalin
Hodder pbk £7.99

Radzinsky, author of an acclaimed life of Nicholas II, turns his attention on the infamous Soviet dictator. He explores his family background, his part (often exaggerated later) in the October Revolution and the fierce ambition and ruthlessness which drove him first to the top of the Communist party and then to the brutal tyranny which kept him in power until his death.

Reed, John
Ten Days That Shook the World
Penguin pbk £6.99
0140182934

The American journalist and Communist activist John Reed (1887 -1920) is one of the few Westerners to be buried in the Heroes' Grave in the Kremlin. His first-hand account of the October Revolution, although it manifests Reed's commitment to the Bolshevik cause and leaders (many of whom were personal friends) and makes little pretence to objectivity, remains an exceptionally lively record of one, very gifted writer's response to the drama of revolution.

Reproduced from *The Oxford Illustrated History of Modern Europe* (Oxford).

Spanish History

Brenan, Gerald
The Spanish Labyrinth
Cambridge UP pbk £7.95
0521398274

Brenan was a writer and friend of several members of the Bloomsbury Group. He lived much of his life in Spain and wrote a number of books on the literature and culture of that country. *The Spanish Labyrinth,* written during and immediately after the Spanish Civil War, has become a classic account of the social and political background to the conflict, enlivened by the vividness with which he describes his own experiences at the time.

Carr, Raymond
Modern Spain 1875-1980
Oxford UP pbk £8.99
0192890905

'Much of modern Spanish history is explained by the tensions caused by the imposition of 'advanced' liberal institutions on an economically and socially 'backward' and conservative society', writes Carr in his intro-duction to this concise account of the subject. He traces these tensions from the 'September Revolution', through the loss of the remnants of empire in the ill-judged war against the USA, through the dictatorship of Primo de Rivera, the ill-fated

Second Republic, the Civil War and the triumph of Francoism, to the return to democracy under Juan Carlos.

Elliott, J.H.
Imperial Spain
Penguin pbk £8.99
0140135170

Spain, from the late fifteenth to early eighteenth centuries, saw a remarkable series of develop-ments. A barren land with a lack of natural advantages, the coun-try rose from 'a mere geographi-cal expression....to an historical fact.' She became the greatest power on earth, possessed of a hugely wealthy empire in the Americas, yet began to lose her impetus and dynamism almost as quickly as she acquired them. Elliott focuses on this period of change and expansion, imperial flowering and imperial decline in this highly readable text.

Kamen, Henry
Spain 1469 -1714
Longman pbk £16.99
0582067235

The period covered by Kamen's book is the most interesting in Spanish history, a period in which the newly unified country acquired a vast overseas empire and the wealth that accompa-nied it. Yet the nation seemed to pass from decades of aggressive

expansionism to decades of comparative decline with few intervening years of stability and security. As Kamen makes clear in this second edition of his valuable textbook, Spain was a society in conflict throughout the period. It was a poor nation suddenly thrust into an imperial role for which it was never fully equipped, and all the major issues of these centuries - the wars in the Netherlands, the activities of the Inquisition, even the unification of the country itself - continued to provoke deep debate and divisions among Spaniards.

Orwell, George
Homage to Catalonia
Penguin pbk £6.99
0140182314

Orwell fought in the Spanish Civil War from December 1936 to July 1937, joining the militia of the POUM (the Workers' Party of Marxist Unity), and wrote this account of his experi-ences soon after returning, wounded, to England. The book is characteristically acute about what he had witnessed and records most tellingly the progress of his disillusionment, from a belief that he was fight-ing on behalf of 'common decency' against the Nationalists and Fascists to the realisation that the Left was venomously divided against itself and that the Soviet-backed forces were determined to destroy the more libertarian POUM and its anarchist allies. Orwell's book deservedly remains the most famous of eye-witness accounts of the war.

Preston, Paul
A Concise History of the Spanish Civil War
Fontana pbk £7.99
0006863736

Preston is an historian who has written a number of academic works on Spain during the Civil War and is the most recent biographer of Franco. In this concise account of the war, aimed at the general reader, he gives an enlightening portrait of the often confused and confusing campaigning and fighting of the war, as well as examining the emergence of Franco's dictatorship from the chaos of nationalist politics, and the extent to which the Spanish War prefigured the global conflict that was to occur in a few years.

Preston, Paul
Franco
HarperCollins pbk £9.99
0006862101

Franco came to power in the Spanish Civil War in the thirties and, by skilfully maintaining Spanish neutrality during the Second World War, avoided the fate of other dictators of the times and continued, despite economic difficulties and quarrels within his own party, to rule the country until his death in 1975. Paul Preston and his huge biography of El Caudillo received widespread praise when it was published in 1993. Although the book, weighing in at more than 1000 pages, may seem forbidding to the non-specialist, Preston has succeeded in shaping his vast researches into a narrative of sustained fascination. This is likely to remain, for years to come, the definitive study of the twentieth century's most successful dictator.

Thomas, Hugh
The Spanish Civil War
Penguin pbk £15.00
0140135936

The battle of ideologies and the conflict in Spain were harbingers of what was to afflict the whole of Europe in World War II. Thomas's hugely detailed and carefully analytical book looks at the confrontations between fascism and democracy, between communism and christianity, between centralism and regionalism that took place in Spain in the thirties. Every aspect of the Civil War - the Spanish Popular Front, the rise of Franco, the intervention of the Soviet Union and Germany, the importance of the Anarchist movement - are examined and assessed in the one indispensable volume on its subject.

A detail from *Guernica* by Pablo Picasso. Reproduced from *The Oxford Illustrated Encyclopedia of World History Volume 2 (Oxford)*.

Other European Countries

Austria

Taylor, A.J.P.
The Hapsburg Monarchy
Penguin pbk £8.99
0140134980

Taylor is at his best in describing the last phase in the long history of the Hapsburgs. Their empire, stretching across central and eastern Europe, confronted them with ultimately insuperable problems, generated by their efforts to provide a heterogeneous population with a peaceful and stable government, unified by a common loyalty. In tracing the efforts of the Hapsburg regime to maintain its position in increasingly hostile historical circumstances, Taylor produced a work which sheds much light on an important area of nineteenth century European history.

Wheatcroft, Andrew
The Hapsburgs
Penguin pbk £8.99
0140236341

Andrew Wheatcroft spent more than twenty years researching this history of the Hapsburgs and the result is an absorbing study of a family that for half a millennium was at the heart of Europe's power structure. His emphasis is strongly on the continuity of the dynasty that the Hapsburgs succeeded in maintaining over the centuries and on the image of that dynasty which they offered to the world, through art works, monuments and ceremonial, to validate their continued power and influence. Their unparalleled record of royal resilience, brought to an end only by the First World War, is clearly traced in this outstanding book.

Bosnia

Malcolm, Noel
Bosnia : A Short History
Papermac pbk £10.00
0333662156

In the last few years the Balkans have been engulfed by a brutal and terrible war. The war is rooted in, but not inevitably determined by, the particular history of the area, a history often misunderstood and wilfully misinterpreted. Noel Malcolm's history of Bosnia from medieval times to the tragedies of the present day is simultaneously a skilful narrative history of a land in which the great powers and great religions of European history have overlapped and combined, and an attempt to clear the fog of historical misunderstanding from a region embroiled in a peculiarly bitter war.

Greece

Clogg, Richard
A Concise History of Modern Greece
Cambridge UP pbk £9.95
0521378303

Vast libraries have been written about Ancient Greek history. Rather less attention has been paid to the modern nation. One of the admirable series of Concise Histories published by Cambridge University Press, Richard Clogg's book is a lucid and well-illustrated introduction to modern Greece, from the first stirrings of the national movement in the late eighteenth century, through the struggle for independence from Turkey, the fledgling nation's varying fortunes in the nineteenth and twentieth centuries, to the present day.

The Netherlands

Boxer, C.R.
The Dutch Seaborne Empire
Penguin pbk £8.99
0140136185

Between 1600 and 1700 the Dutch, through the trading of the Dutch East India Company and the Dutch West India Company, and through the enterprise of their navigators and explorers, built up a large overseas empire. Trading centres and colonies developed in the East Indies, at the Cape, on the eastern coasts of South America and at the mouth of the Hudson where New York was originally New Amsterdam. Boxer's book is a standard work on the growth of this mercantile empire and of its decline during the eighteenth century.

Parker, Geoffrey
The Dutch Revolt
Penguin pbk £7.99
0140137122
Beginning in 1550 and continuing for many decades the Dutch, driven by a complex mixture of political, economic and, above all, religious motives, conducted a bloody struggle for independence from Spain which resulted in the Hapsburgs losing power in the Low Countries and in the creation of the Dutch Republic. Geoffrey Parker's account of the revolt combines an enthralling narrative with a lucid examination of the historical debates and issues involved. His work remains the most detailed and most reliable exposition of the various stages in the development of the revolt.

Schama, Simon
The Embarrassment of Riches
Fontana pbk £16.99
0006861369
When this book was first published the TLS described it as 'an event in historical studies and Schama is a historian of rare

standing and exceptional qualities'. Schama skilfully combines an erudite social and cultural investigation of how an assortment of communities in the Low Countries with no shared language, religion or government, transformed themselves in the 17th century into the world power of the Dutch Republic, with a talent for narrative and an eye for character that draw in the general reader. Not the least of the book's many merits is its superb use of illustrative material and Schama's deftness at unravelling the iconographic meanings and resonances of even the most apparently homely of Dutch genre painting in the period.

Poland

Davies, Norman
The Heart of Europe
Oxford UP pbk £11.99
0192851527
Davies, the author of the recent and highly acclaimed *Europe: A History*, wrote his history of Poland in the early eighties at a time when the country was once again undergoing upheaval and social division as Solidarity flourished and martial law was imposed to prevent its further successes. Using an unconventional approach, Davies moves backward in time in successive chapters to reveal the social and political inheritance of modern Poland and to set recent events in the longer perspective of a series of Russo-Polish conflicts stretching back nearly three centuries.

Zamoyski, Adam
The Polish Way
John Murray pbk £15.99
0719546745
Zamoyski's achievement in this book is to place the history of Poland over a thousand years, from the 10th century to the present, in a broader European context and to trace, beneath the obvious discontinuities of that history, an underlying continuity. Too often historians have been preoccupied by the undoubted woes which have beset the Poles and have ignored or downplayed their achievements. Zamoyski redresses that balance in his account.

Portugal

Birmingham, David
A Concise History of Portugal
Cambridge UP pbk £9.95
0521438802
This volume provides a succinct account of Portuguese history, paying particular attention to the society and people from which, after the Treaty of Tordesillas, the empire in the Americas sprang, to the period of Spanish dominion in the late sixteenth and early seventeenth centuries and to the rule of the House of Braganza after the nationalist revolution. The book also considers Portugal's often troubled history in more recent times, the long dictatorial rule of Salazar, the bloody dissolution of their African empire and their return to democracy and entry into the European community.

World History – General

Ariès, Phillippe
Centuries of Childhood
Pimlico pbk £12.50
0712674586

In the Middle Ages childhood was not thought to be a stage of life radically distinct from adulthood. Children were dressed, addressed and thought of as miniature adults. In the following centuries the idea of childhood as a quite separate phase of life developed and it is the gradual rise of this idea that Ariès charts in his pioneering study. Using the evidence of art and iconography, and teasing out the assumptions and concepts present in contemporary religious and educational writings, Aries presents a fascinating survey of attitudes to children and to family life through the centuries.

Aries, Philippe & Duby, Georges (eds)
A History of Private Life
Harvard UP

I. From Pagan Rome to Byzantium
pbk £11.95
0674399749

II. Revelations of the Medieval World
pbk £11.95
0674400011

III. Passions of the Renaissance
pbk £11.95
067440002X

IV. From the Fires of Revolution to the Great War
pbk £12.50
0674400038

V. Riddles of Identity in Modern Times
pbk £12.50
0674400046

In this sumptuously illustrated series of books, an array of well-known scholars turn their attention on past attitudes to the concerns of private, rather than public life - attitudes to sex and the family, to the organisation of domesticity, to the relationships between social equals and the relationships between different classes, to the quotidian affairs of ordinary life. The five volumes cover a great sweep of history from the ancient world and the transition from paganism to Christianity to the dramatic revolutions in nationality, class, family and religion in this century. Although meticulous in their scholarship, the writers assume curiosity about the past in their readers rather than a vast pre-existing erudition.

Belchem, John & Price, Richard(eds)
Dictionary of Nineteenth Century History
Penguin pbk £9.99
0140512691

Containing more than eight hundred entries, this dictionary is an authoritative and up-to-date guide to the political, military, social, economic and cultural history of the century which witnessed the Industrial Revolution, the advent of liberalism and socialism, the growth of nationalism and huge advances in scientific and technological knowledge. The dictionary is international in scope and pays due attention to areas outside Europe and North America, as well as acknowledging the achievements of women in the period and of African-American and Native American figures.

Black, Jeremy & Porter, Roy (eds)
Dictionary of Eighteenth Century History
Penguin pbk £9.99
0140512586

Edited by two of the foremost historians of the period, this dictionary is one of the few available which covers not only the century's major events and personalities in Europe and America but also includes entries drawn from the internal histories of Africa, China and other cultures of the time. Cultural context is provided by the entries on the arts and philosophy, surveys of the latest debates on controversial subjects demonstrate the range of historical thinking on the period and the maps and dynastic charts, the bibliography and chronology complete an essential reference work.

Braudel, Fernand
A History of Civilizations
Penguin pbk £9.99
0140124896

Braudel was one of the century's greatest historians and, throughout his work, rejected narrow notions of what history should be and what the intellectual sources upon which the historian ought to draw should be. *A History of Civilizations*, the last of his books to be translated into English, exemplifies this rejection and is characteristically ambitious in its scope. It is a survey of broad historical developments in nearly every corner of the world : in the Muslim world, from the rise of Islam to post-colonial revival, in the Far East, in Europe from the collapse of the Roman empire to political union, in the new worlds created by European expansion and colonialism and in the 'other' Europe dominated, until recently, by the Soviet Union.

Fernandez-Armesto, Felipe
Millennium
Transworld pbk £14.99
0552994820

This much-acclaimed book presents a refreshingly wide-ranging and intelligent perspective on the last thousand years of man's history. Adopting the viewpoint of an imaginary future observer of the last millennium allows Fernandez-Armesto the opportunity to cover world history at the level of entire civilizations and cultures while not losing sight of the telling detail. Vivid writing and hundreds of illustrations make this book the most exciting work of global history currently available.

Foucault, Michel
The History of Sexuality Volume 1
Penguin pbk £6.99
0140124748

The History of Sexuality Volume 2
Penguin pbk £9.99
0140137343

The History of Sexuality Volume 3
Penguin pbk £8.99
0140137351

A social scientist and historian of ideas, Foucault (1926 - 1984) was one of the most important and influential intellectual figures of the contemporary world. His *History of Sexuality* is an ambitious attempt to explore the changing nature of desire through the centuries. Volume One, An Introduction, states his intended methodology and challenges the notion that the nineteenth century was sexually repressive, arguing instead that discussion about sex has been gathering momentum since the seventeenth century. Far from making us more liberated, however, this analysis seems more about making a science out of sex. Volume Two, *The Use of Pleasure*, discusses the emergence of Christianity from the Ancient World and the differences and continuities in sexual behaviour that can be detected in this emergence. Volume Three, *The Care of the Self*, discusses Roman sexual discourse, again demonstrating just how dramatically attitudes can change.

Columbus's ship on his voyage of 1492. Reproduced from *The Oxford Illustrated History of Europe* (Oxford).

History is like a nymph glimpsed bathing between leaves. The more you shift your point of view, the more is revealed. If you want to see her whole, you have to be prepared to try a lot of different perspectives.

Our traditional understanding of the world has been warped by the way we have looked at it. Historians of the future, looking back with new priorities and prejudices of their own, may hardly notice the events which have seemed world-shaping to us. We can try to anticipate them by re-examining supposedly formative moments from our past from an unusual angle. Imagine, for instance, a cosmic observer looking down on our world from an astral height at intervals in the last thousand years in 1097, say, 1497, 1797 and 1997. What would grab this privileged scrutineer's attention?

Felipe Fernandez-Armesto

The Cosmic Observer's View

The author of *Millennium* looks at some formative dates from the past from an unusual angle

1097.... In 1997 more than nine centuries have passed since the start of the First Crusade 'this manifold and great awakening and campaign of Christian people', as one crusader called it, 'to fight on God's behalf.' In the light of western Europe's later performance in world-wide land-grabbing, it is not surprising that this moment came to be seen as a turning-point, when European expansion began in earnest. Yet, from sufficiently far-off in space and time, the crusaders' achievements would look like a flea-bite on the hide of Islam. Except for the ruins of their castles, few of their effects lingered. They played a part in world history less as a threat to Islam than as a stimulus to its resurgence by provoking a form of irredentism deeply dyed in religious self-awareness.

Our hypothetical observer, moreover, would attach less importance to the temporary divisions between rival caliphates and ethnic enemies than to the long-term accession of strength that Islam derived from the absorption of steppeland invaders. From any viewpoint other than a westerner's, the integration of the Turks into the Islamic world seems to be much more significant than the crusaders' brief passage through it which is no more worthy of notice than the temporary checks imposed, in other directions, by Rajput princes, Georgian imperialism, Soninke power in west Africa and local politics in Spain.

1497... Four hundred years later, Columbus was consolidating his achievement in crossing the Atlantic and establishing the first European colony in the New World. The opening of America to European influence was hailed in the next generation as 'the greatest event since the creation of the world save only for the incarnation of Him Who made it.' Judged by the cumulative effect of all the Atlantic crossings which followed for the next five hundred years, this was indeed a new departure in world history, which shifted ideas, biota, people and power with greater impact than ever before. But, at the time, our cosmic observer would have been busy monitoring two more conspicuous phenomena of expansion : those of the Ottoman and Muscovite empires.

Over a longer perspective than that of the mere five hundred years at our disposal, the expansion of Muscovy may come to seem more noteworthy than the establishment of transatlantic links. For the seaborne empires founded in the wake of Columbus have all disappeared and much of their legacy has been repudiated. While Columbus was battering resistance and building shrines in Hispaniola, Muscovite expeditions were campaigning on the Ob, launching the most enduring episode of European expansion in modern history, which eventually extended the territory of Russia to the Arctic and Pacific Oceans. In consequence, the Russians today are by far the most numerous of European peoples, with under-exploited resources at their disposal which make them potentially the most powerful, too. If, as seems likely, Europe finally succumbs to Russian domination at some time fairly early in the next millennium, the cosmic observer of 1497 will be vindicated and the fate of the Komi will seem more interesting than that of the Caribs.

1797... In 1797, the campaigns of citizen-armies emphatically proclaimed the virtues of French Revolutionary ideas. Though the armies were soon rolled back, the ideas lasted and spread. Many heirs of the Revolution all over the world have shared the contemporary illusion that it was 'the greatest event that ever happened in the world, and how much the best!' Meanwhile the eyes of our astral observer would surely have been riveted on China.

In the long term the ideas of Confucius will probably be judged more important in shaping the history of the world than those of Rousseau or Voltaire. If so, the phenomenal expansion of early-modern China will be partly responsible. Though most world-history books concentrate on European empire-building in the period, that of China was far more significant in terms of the numbers of people subjected, the durability of the changes effected and the cohesion of the new Chinese identity and statehood which were imposed.

The check to Chinese expansion, with the madness and death of the Ch'ien-lung emperor, at about the same time as the French revolutionary armies were beginning their careers of conquest, can genuinely be said to have diverted world history into a new course. For nearly two hundred years China remained, in Napoleon's words, 'a slumbering giant': the great age of western hegemonies coincided with this exceptional period of Chinese quiescence. Now both are coming to an end.

1997.... I suspect, therefore, that the cosmic observer of 1997 is not sharing our current satisfaction with the apparently almost world-wide triumph of western liberal politics and economics. He (or, perhaps, by now, she) will notice the abiding divisions and looming conflicts of our planet rather than the superficial globalisation that captures our attention. And the world will seem to be reverting to its normal state: with world-shaping initiatives again emerging from east Asia, where the greatest concentration of human resources continues to be housed, and from where, during most of history, the richest promises and the gravest threats have spread.

the next twenty years led inexorably to a further war of mass destruction. From the second war came a world order overshadowed by the implacable hostility of two superpowers. The changes wrought by the fall of the Iron Curtain and the break-up of the Soviet Union are the subject of a new chapter added to the revised edition of this stimulating book.

Johnson, Paul
A History of the Jews
Phoenix pbk £9.99
1857993802

'No history of a people', writes Paul Johnson, 'has more to teach mankind than the long, tragic yet exhilarating story of the Jews.' Johnson's book is not only a survey of 4,000 years of Jewish history but an investigation of the impact of Jewish genius and imagination on the world.

Johnson, Paul
Modern Times
Phoenix pbk £9.99
1857994507

Johnson's ambitious history of the world from the twenties to the nineties of this century is characterised by the intelligence, wide reading and forceful opinions which mark all his work. Beginning with a world in which, in the aftermath of the First World War, the traditional European order had been destroyed and the first Marxist state established, Johnson shows how the emergence of fascism in

Kennedy, Paul
The Rise and Fall of the Great Powers
Fontana pbk £12.99
0006860524

On first publication of *The Rise and Fall of the Great Powers*, Christopher Hitchens claimed in the Guardian 'This book is falling out of briefcases all over Washington DC'. In writing a volume designed to be read by policy makers and lay reader alike, Kennedy seems to set himself an impossibly grand task, only to demonstrate a capacity to construct an exploration of five centuries of Empire-building and collapse that is both rigorous and readable. Despite the vast sweep of time and political and economic history explored, the book shows a clarity and simplicity that is a tribute to Kennedy's intelligent and original approach. It is heartening to consider that Kennedy's examination of the relationship between military power and economic strength has generated both personal and public debate; it should indeed be required reading for all those public figures with a hand in our future.

Kinder & Hilgemann
Penguin Atlas of World History Volume 1
Penguin pbk £8.99
0140510540

Penguin Atlas of World History Volume 2
Penguin pbk £8.99
0140512896

These two volumes have long been a useful reference work in which clear maps and illustrations are placed alongside a chronological summary of the main political cultural and religious events in world history. The first volume covers the long sweep of history from prehistory to the eve of the French Revolution. The second volume deals with the complicated developments of the last two hundred years.

McNeill, William
Plagues and Peoples
Penguin pbk £8.99
0140233644

Profesor McNeill's book describes the impact of infectious diseases, from smallpox to influenza, on the rise and fall of civilizations. Epidemic diseases could have a devastating effect on societies, destroying great empires like those of the Aztecs and Incas who were decimated by plagues brought by the Spaniards, ruined by European diseases as much as by European arms. As we confront AIDS in contemporary societies, McNeill's book gathers greater resonance and relevance.

Miles, Rosalind
Women's History of the World
HarperCollins pbk £7.99
0586088865

Men have dominated the historical record because, until recently, they have been responsible for creating it. Much valuable work has been undertaken in recent decades to rectify the imbalance and Rosalind Miles' ambitious volume is successful in synthesising much of that work into a general history that records both the lives of ordinary women through the centuries and the stories of those remarkable individual women, often unjustly ignored, who made a significant impact on history. The book overturns many entrenched preconceptions and, as Antonia Fraser wrote at the time of its first publication, it was 'written to alleviate a genuine injustice.'

Overy, R.J.
Times Atlas of the Twentieth Century
Times Books Hbk £25.00
0723007667

This is a major historical atlas which interweaves text, maps and illustration to bring this century's main themes and underlying problems sharply into focus. Taking us from the cataclysm of the First World War to the uncertainties of the present day, the book combines 250 full-colour maps with more than 350 complementary illustrations to create a beautifully produced volume that is also a substantial work of scholarship.

Roberts, J. M.
Penguin History of the World
Penguin pbk £12.99
0140154957

To encompass the whole sweep of human history in one-volume, even one of more than a thousand pages, is massively ambitious but Roberts, in this lucid and wide-ranging account, showed himself equal to the task. When it was first published A.J.P. Taylor described it as 'a stupendous achievement' and went on to call it 'the unrivalled World History for our day.' This is an accolade which it continues to deserve.

Schama, Simon
Landscape and Memory
HarperCollins pbk £20.00
0006863485

This is a strikingly original work of historical investigation, hard to pigeonhole, once read, even harder to forget. Schama's study centres on our relationship with landscape and the natural world and on the interdependence of landscape and culture. Each shapes the other, Schama argues, claiming that our scenery is built up 'as much from strata of memory as from layers of rock.' Drawing on a vast array of evidence and sources, Schama explores the histories of such concepts as the forest primeval and the river of life and shows how they continue to influence the way we see landscapes today.

Segal, Ronald
The Black Diaspora
Faber pbk £9.99
0571178022
Segal's own moral vision and intellect are in evidence throughout this history spanning five centuries. Beginning in Africa, before the arrival of the slave trade, the book then explores the changes wrought on societies devastated by a trade which shipped over 10 million people across the Atlantic. Segal casts his ironic and politically astute eye across the actual development of the trade, records the resistance of slaves, the poverty and discimination that ensued after emancipation, and the continuing hostility and discrimination manifest in avowedly democratic nations. He sets himself an enormous task - and with clarity, a firm and unsentimental style and the capacity to convey the significance of every historical detail, he succeeds. *The Black Diaspora* continues up until the present day, and it has inevitable resonances both for now and the future; his is a record not just of victimisation and suffering, but of courage, resilience and a heritage worth fighting for. In Segal's own words; 'There were no slaves in the caves. It took civilization to create the concept of people as property. The supreme paradox of human history is that it has brought, along with much light, a deepening of the dark.'

The Times Atlas of World History
Times Books hbk £40.00
0723005346

The Times Concise Atlas of World History
Times Books pbk £14.95
0723006741
For many years the Times Atlas has been acknowledged as the most authoritative and beautifully produced collection of maps illustrating world history that is available. The most recent edition covers every major event in several thousand years in more than 600 full colour maps and photographs, which illuminate a huge array of historical subjects from Ancient Greece to the collapse of the Soviet Union. Each map is accompanied by lucid and concise commentary.

Wells, H.G.
A Short History of the World
Penguin pbk £7.99
0140184384
Wells, novelist and polymath, produced this history in 1922 and the Penguin Modern Classic edition is a reprinting of the original edition. His brief history of civilization takes the reader, in a little over three hundred pages, from man's origins to the end of the First World War. Wells's skill as a novelist is evident in his precise and vigorous prose and in the succinctness of the narrative, which he builds around his central theme of the progress of ideas - the cultural impact of man's developing knowledge of the natural world and the gradual evolution of political institutions.

Zeldin, Theodore
An Intimate History of Humanity
Minerva pbk £7.99
0749396237
Zeldin writes about the history which is alive in people's minds today in this internationally acclaimed investigation of emotions and personal relationships, both past and present. The structure of the work is ambitious and original. Each chapter begins with a pen portrait of a living person whose thoughts and emotions, desires and regrets are then explored within a long historical perspective. The result is a book which one critic declared was 'the most exciting and ambitious work of non-fiction I have read in more than a decade'.

Ancient Civilisations – General

Allegro, John
The Dead Sea Scrolls
Penguin pbk £7.99
0140134573
In 1947 the chance discovery by a shepherd boy of ancient texts, which had apparently been hidden in caves in the arid cliffs above the Dead Sea, led to fresh light being thrown on the relationship between Judaism and early Christianity. The scrolls, which include copies of Old Testament books up to a thousand years older than previously known versions, have since been the object of close scrutiny and, often, heated scholarly debate. John Allegro was one of those scholars most closely involved in the interpretation and publication of the scrolls - and most flamboyantly involved in the controversy - and his book, although in print for many years, remains an invaluable and fascinating contribution to the ongoing debate about them.

Cotterell, Arthur
Penguin Encyclopedia of Ancient Civilisations
Penguin pbk £15.00
0140114343
This encyclopedia encompasses the flowering of ancient Greece and Rome but its greatest strength is its breadth of scope, including as it does ancient Persia, India and China which are so often neglected by textbooks on the ancient world. The imaginative use of maps, plans and photographic illustrations enlivens the text and makes the book suitable for a wide readership, allowing the reader to build a secure knowledge of chronology and how the development of these cultures related one to another.

Mason, J. Alden
Ancient Civilisations of Peru
Penguin pbk £9.99
0140135227
Recently archaeologists have found evidence of cultures and civilizations in Peru dating far back into the past. Radiocarbon dating has placed the first signs of emerging societies as early as 7,500 B.C., more than nine thousand years before the devastations wrought on the mature Inca empire by Pizarro and his invading Spanish conquistadors. This substantial survey by J. Alden Mason is the best introduction for the non-specialist to the rich discoveries made about Ancient Peru.

Rohl, David
A Test of Time
Arrow pbk £14.99
0099365618
In 1995 David Rohl presented a TV series which put forward the challenging views of Ancient Egyptian chronology and Old Testament history that he has developed in over twenty years of research. This book, an elaboration of the TV series, makes clear the extent to which his views, if accepted, would overturn the academic disciplines of Egyptology and Near Eastern archaeology. Most scholars in these fields would argue that the narratives of the Old Testament should be treated with extreme scepticism as historical documents. One of the chief reasons for such scepticism is that, despite much endeavour, archaeologists have unearthed very little corroborative evidence for biblical traditions. In this fascinating and well-illustrated volume, Rohl argues persuasively that the reason for this failure is that archaeologists, misled by an incorrect chronology for ancient history, drawn from mis-interpreted Egyptian sources, have been looking in the right place for the evidence but at the wrong time.

Romer, John

Seven Wonders of the World

Michael O'Mara pbk £10.99
1854796763

Who has not heard of the
Colossus of Rhodes or the
Hanging Gardens of Babylon?
The Seven Wonders of the
World were first listed two
thousand years ago and yet they
remain a source of fascination
to this day. The internationally
renowned archaeologist John
Romer subtitles his authoritative
and highly illustrated book
*A History of the Modern
Imagination,* and his work
describes the legends associated
with the wonders and the ways
in which they have lodged in
the imagination of Western
civilization, as well as the reality
of the monuments and buildings
themselves.

Roux, Georges

Ancient Iraq

Penguin pbk £9.99
014012523X

Over the last hundred years
archaeologists have unearthed
the monuments and texts of a
number of civilizations that
flourished in ancient times in
the lands between the Tigris and
the Euphrates, civilizations that
were previously known only
through allusions in the Bible.
In this major work, now in its
third edition, Roux traces the
rise and fall of the Sumerians
and Akkadians, the Babylonians
and the Assyrians, examines
their institutions and religions
and reviews what can be uncovered about their daily lives.

Scarre (ed)

**Past Worlds: The Times Atlas
of Archaeology**

Times Books hbk £35.00
0723008108

Incorporating hundreds of
maps, illustrations, photographs
and reconstructions of ancient
sites, this book is a fundamental
reference work for anyone interested in archaeology. From the
origins of mankind to the era of
the Industrial Revolution, the
atlas reveals details of sites and
artefacts from all over the world.

Schnapp, Alain

The Discovery of the Past

British Museum Press hbk £25.00
0714117684

This is an ambitious, well-produced and highly-illustrated
investigation of the ways in
which mankind, from antiquity
to the 19th century, has become

conscious of, and has responded
to the past and its surviving
relics. It looks closely at the way
the past has been used as a
means of both understanding
and manipulating the present.

Reproduced from the *Illustrated History of Europe*
(Weidenfeld & Nicolson).

Ancient Egypt

Edwards, I. E.
The Pyramids of Egypt
Penguin pbk £9.99
0140136347

First published as long ago as 1947 but extensively revised in 1993, Edwards' survey of a thousand years of pyramid-building in Egypt, from the earliest mastabas of the first and second dynasties to the famous group at Giza, is a definitive work which draws on his own experience as an Egyptologist and the work of the many archaeologists who have excavated in the Nile Valley. It describes clearly and concisely the principal features of a number of pyramids which illustrate the evolution and subsequent decline of that eerily grand style of tomb-making. The book is illustrated by black and white photographs and a number of diagrams and plans.

Grimal, Nicolas
History of Ancient Egypt
Blackwell pbk £12.99
0631193960

Over the last three decades there has been an ever-increasing amount of archaeological material emerging from sites in Egypt, as well as new linguistic discoveries and growing debate and discussion about the chronology within which these should be sited. A new synthesis of all this evidence was needed and a new account of the rise and fall of civilization in the Nile Valley which would incorporate it. In this scholarly but accessible text, covering the period from the first human settlements to the conquest by Alexander the Great in 333 B.C. , Nicolas Grimal has provided that and produced an elegant account of the political, economic and cultural history of the Egyptians within the framework of a tightly argued chronology.

Murnane, William
Penguin Guide to Ancient Egypt
Penguin pbk £16.00
0140469524

A skilful combination of practical guide to the major monuments and sites of Ancient Egypt with a concise cultural history, Murnane's book provides the reader and traveller with descriptions of what remains to be seen today, and insights into the functions these monuments served in the lives of those who built and used them. The new and updated edition covers not only Pharaonic remains but also Christian sites and the Islamic monuments around Cairo. Sites only recently opened to the public are also included and the book examines many of the finest antiquities and *objets d'art* housed in the major museums of the country.

Manley, Bill
The Penguin Historical Atlas of Ancient Egypt
Penguin pbk £9.99
0140513310

In more than sixty colour maps, which make use of the latest archaeological scholarship and evidence, this atlas traces the history and culture of Egypt from the founding of Memphis in 5000 B.C. , through the rise to economic success and advanced civilisation, the artistic and cultural triumphs under Akhenaten, Tutankhamun and Ramesses II, to the period of Greek domination and the final collapse under the Roman Empire.

Noblecourt, Christian
Tutankhamen
Penguin pbk £14.00
0140116656

The discovery by Howard Carter in 1922 of the tomb of the boy pharaoh Tutankhamen remains the single most important archaeological find of the century. The find, and the

Reeves, Nicholas & Wilkinson, Richard

The Complete Valley of the Kings

Thames & Hudson hbk £19.95
0500050805

The Valley of the Kings is the valley near ancient Thebes where the pharoahs of the New Kingdom were buried. This book by Reeves and Wilkinson describes all the eighty tombs of the valley and considers the art, archaeology and history of this ancient necropolis.

Shaw, Ian & Nicholson, Paul

British Museum Dictionary of Ancient Egypt

British Museum Press hbk £27.00
0714109827

Who was Osiris? How were the pyramids constructed? Why did Tutankhamun change his name? The answers to these and many other questions about four thousand years of Ancient Egyptian civilization can be found in this book, the most up-to-date and comprehensive reference work on the subject for the general reader. Highly illustrated with photographs, maps and charts, distinguished by the imprimatur of the British Museum, this is a mine of information on the events, ideas and personalities of Ancient Egypt.

resultant publicity, transformed a relatively obscure pharaoh of the eighteenth dynasty, who had probably died while still in his teens, into the most famous of all Ancient Egyptians, and heralded a rise in interest in Egyptology. This large-format, well-illustrated book by a distinguished French archaeologist provides an excellent guide to the tomb and the nature and purpose of the precious objects found within it.

Reeves, Nicholas

The Complete Tutankhamun

Thames & Hudson pbk £12.95
0500278105

This is the fullest account ever published of the world's greatest archaeological discovery. The book includes double-page features on each stage of the discovery, extracts from Howard Carter's own notes and diaries, background on Tutankhamun himself and the times in which he lived, a full reference section, a rich array of photographs and illustrations, and fresh evidence from recent scholarly work on the fantastic and beautiful artefacts unearthed by Carter and his colleagues.

Tyldesley, Joyce

Daughters of Isis

Penguin pbk £8.99
0140175962

Drawing on all the available sources, this readable book reconstructs the lives of Egyptian women in the period from 3000 to 300 B.C., paying particular attention to marriage and sexuality, domestic life, political influence and religious observation. Perhaps surprisingly, Tyldesley argues, and skilfully marshals the evidence to support her argument, that Egyptian women enjoyed a remarkable legal, social and sexual independence which was lost in later societies.

Nicholas Reeves

Unlocking the Secrets of the Valley of the Kings

The author of *The Complete Tutankhamun* and *The Complete Valley of the Kings* describes the excitement of recent discoveries in Egypt

Egyptology rarely makes the front cover of Time magazine, but in May 1995 it did. There, staring out at the reader, were the impassive features, carved in wood, of Ramesses the Great, pharoah of Egypt more than three thousand years ago. 'Secrets of the Lost Tombs' proclaimed the headline referring not, as it turned out, to the king's own tomb in the Valley of the Kings (which has lain open since antiquity), but to that of his fifty or more sons nearby. Kent Weeks, an American Egyptologist, had been painstakingly investigating this tomb, prosaically known as KV5 since 1987, and had suddenly broken through into an extraordinary corridor, off which lay innumerable 'burial chapels' for Ramesses's sons. Who knew what further surprises, and indeed treasures, might be in store?

Not since the discovery of Tutankhamun's tomb in 1922 has there been such worldwide interest in the Valley of the Kings. No fewer than eight international teams are currently working in the royal valley, and two million visitors a year make the pilgrimage to this ancient necropolis at Thebes. But what exactly does this cemetery consist of and why the eternal fascination with it?

The site was for five hundred years the last resting place for Egypt's New Kingdom Pharoahs (in the Old Kingdom, Egyptian rulers had been buried beneath pyramids further north along the Nile). The Valley of the Kings stands without equal as the most magnificent burial ground the world has ever seen. Here, in a dried-up river valley dominated by a pyramid-shaped peak sacred to the goddess Hathor, Egyptian workers toiled in the desert heat to quarry eight or more tombs for their rulers and nobility. The walls of many of these sepulchres were decorated from top to bottom with wonderful paintings, mysterious guides to the Underworld, and their chambers filled to overflowing with incredible treasures - gilded coffins and shrines, jewels, unguents, chariots, couches, weapons: all the paraphernalia of ritual and daily life needed by the deceased in the next world. At the focal point of the tomb, in the burial chamber within the innermost coffin of an enclosing sarcophagus, lay the royal mummy, carried in a ritual procession from Thebes to its eternal resting place.

As things turned out, however, for the mummies and their treasures, this was but a beginning. Tomb-robbing is not a modern innovation, but was a profitable pursuit even in New Kingdom times. The thefts became so widespread that, in desperation, at the close of the era, a thousand years before Christ, it was decided to gather together the royal mummies and re-inter them for safe-keeping in secret burial caches in the cliffs overlooking the Theban plain. The story of tomb-robbing in the valley, and the extraordinary rediscovery of the mummy caches a century ago, have been the focus of my own researches over the past twenty years.

So far there has been no single, up-to-date and general account attempting to tell the full story of the royal necropolis : who built it, how and why; its rise and fall over half a millennium; who plundered it and who rediscovered it. This is the aim of *The Complete Valley of the Kings :Tombs and Treasures of Egypt's Greatest Pharoahs*, which I co-authored with fellow Egyptologist Richard Wilkinson. Richard is director of the University of Arizona Egyptian Expedition, which is currently investigating several tombs in the valley. We readily admit that the adjective 'complete' may raise a few eyebrows but we try to cover every aspect of the story, and a major feature of our book is that it describes all the tombs, not just a few, and provides factfiles of essential information as well as cutaway perspective views specially created for the book of all the royal tombs. So we hope it will appeal not only to dedicated Egyptian enthusiasts (of whom there are an ever-growing number), but also to those who simply want to visit Thebes and need a well-signposted overview. Specifically for tourists, we provide a brief guide of when to go and what to see.

The excavation and exploration of KV5 by Kent Weeks and his team are continuing as I write, and are bound to generate more international headlines over the coming months. Only recently Weeks discovered two unexpected and unique corridors that seem to lead from the royal sons' tombs in the direction of Ramesses the Great's own sepulchre. But, in a valley so well explored, are there really further mysteries to resolve, new discoveries to be made? The answer is an emphatic yes. The hunt is still on for the tombs of the shadowy Smenkhare, predecessor of Tutankhamun and the equally elusive Ramesses VIII. (I have my own hunch as to where archaeologists should look for Smenkhare.) And the heated debate amongst Egyptologists about the true identity of the occupant of Tomb 55 (linked in some fashion with the heretic pharoah Akhenaten) looks set to run for a few years yet. The Valley of the Kings has by no means yielded up all its secrets.

African History

Bernal, Martin
Black Athena
Vintage pbk £8.99
0099887800

What is classical about classical civilization? In a revolutionary work of scholarship Bernal challenges the basis of our thinking about this question and argues that the roots of much of what we continue to admire in Ancient Greek culture and philosophy, which has had such a profound impact on the civilization of the West, lie in Afro-Asiatic cultures. He suggests further that, since the eighteenth century, there has been, among scholars in the West, a systematic denial of these roots, largely for racist reasons, and he provides substantial evidence, drawn from a vast array of sources, to support his controversial thesis.

Davidson, Basil
Modern Africa
Longman pbk £13.99
058221288X

Basil Davidson is one of the best known and most admired of historians of Africa and this well respected text is his own particular contribution to the debates about the origins of the new African states, the conflicts and crises that they have faced in their short but often turbulent existences, and the solutions that might emerge for what often seem wholly intractable problems. His review of the varying fortunes of African nationalism and African nationalists in the transformation of colonies into independent states is always stimulating and he undertakes a fair-minded assessment of the continuing relationship between the developed world and its former possessions.

Iliffe, John
Africans : The Story of a Continent
Cambridge UP pbk £12.95
0521484227

This is an introduction to the broad sweep of African history from the origins of mankind to the South African general election of 1994. Iliffe constructs a narrative which incorporates the main subjects of African history - for example the impacts of Islam and Christianity, the depredations of the Atlantic slave trade, colonial invasions and the challenges of recent independence - into a text that is stimulating and wide-ranging. 'The central themes of African history', writes Iliffe, 'are the peopling of the continent, the achievement of human coexistence with nature, the building up of enduring societies, and their defence against more favoured regions.' His book amply illustrates these themes.

McEvedy, Colin
Atlas of African History
Penguin pbk £7.99
0140513213

Africa, the continent which gave birth to the human species, has had a turbulent history in which long, nomadic movements of peoples have contrasted with the creation of permanent states and major civilizations - Egypt, Mali, Benin and Great Zimbabwe. African contact with other peoples, particularly Europeans, has not been a happy experience, although in the twentieth century Africa has found the leaders it needed to re-establish lost independences and create the nation-states of today. Using the format successfully established by his previous atlases, McEvedy records this history in 59 maps and accompanying text.

Moorehead, Alan
The Blue Nile
Penguin pbk £13.00
014006673X

The White Nile
Penguin pbk £13.00
0140036849

Alan Moorehead's two volumes on the greatest river in Africa, the cultures that depend upon it and, particularly, the European explorers who strove to reach the sources of the Blue Nile and the White Nile, together make up a riveting work of popular history. Moorehead traces the two branches of the Nile from the Ethiopian highlands to the sea, from the Mountains of the Moon to the Mediterranean and tells the dramatic stories of its often eccentric but always determined Victorian explorers - Sir Richard Burton who, before setting out to explore the Nile, had made a pilgrimage to Mecca disguised as a Pathan, John Hanning Speke, who died in a mysterious shooting accident and is commemorated by an obelisk in Kensington Gardens, and Sir Samuel Baker, who took his new, Hungarian-born wife on a four-year expedition into the African hinterland.

Morris, Donald
The Washing of the Spears
Pimlico pbk £12.50
0712661050

This is a history book on a grand scale which tells of the astonishingly precipitous rise of the Zulus under Shaka, the military genius who created their empire in southern Africa, and of their equally sudden downfall, fifty years after Shaka's death, in the war forced upon them by the British. The early success of the Zulus at the Battle of Isandhlwana, a success which appalled Victorian Britain, the heroic defence of Rorke's Drift by a handful of British soldiers confronted by the victorious Zulu impis, and the final outcome, tragic but inevitable, of a struggle between the assegai and the Gatling gun, are all covered in detail by Morris's book. It also provides the reader with an immensely knowledgeable account of British policy, both colonial and military, in southern Africa and of those individuals involved in it.

Oliver, Roland
The African Experience
Pimlico pbk £10.00
071698698

Professor Oliver is one of the most distinguished of historians of Africa and in this book he rises magnificently to the challenge of encompassing the entire span of human history in the continent, from the earliest hominids discovered in the Olduvai Gorge to the disintegration of apartheid in South Africa, in little more than 250 pages. Brief but illuminating attention is paid to a range of subjects – the formation and diffusion of African languages, the impact of Islam and Christianity, the slave trade, the scramble for colonies by the European powers in the nineteenth century and the emergence of modern nation states – in a book which is an ideal introduction to African history.

Poster published by the African National Congress reproduced from *The Oxford Illustrated Encyclopedia of World History* (Oxford).

Oliver & Fage
A Short History of Africa
Penguin pbk £7.99
0140136010
The sixth edition of this firmly
established work draws on the
full range of literature about
the continent, and upon the
evidence provided by archaeology, oral traditions and linguistic
research, to create a readable
narrative of African history. Too
often African history has been
seen only in its interactions with
European history and, although
Oliver & Fage recognise that
parts of the continent's history
can only be understood in terms
of resistance and subjection to
European aggression, they also
recognise the importance of
approaching many events from
a wholly African perspective.

Pakenham, Thomas
The Scramble for Africa
Abacus pbk £12.99
0349104492
The Scramble for Africa is
the name usually given to the
phase of European imperialism
between 1875 and 1900 which
saw the increasingly rapid
acquisition and division of
African territory by the major
European powers. Pakenham's
book is a superb study of this
phase. He makes clear how
much of the expansion was
fortuitous - all the powers
seeking advantage in Africa
were driven as much by concern
over what their rivals were doing
as any strong desire for new
colonies. Only Leopold, the
King of the Belgians, who saw
the opportunity to place his
country (and, more importantly,
himself) at the centre of one
international stage, seemed to
know clearly what he wanted.
African resistance to European
incursion took various forms but
only Ethiopia managed to retain
its independence. The story of
this *folie de grandeur* on the part
of the European powers is wide
ranging and complex but
Pakenham has written a book
that, in its telling mix of narrative
and analysis, makes sense of it.

Thompson, Leonard
History of South Africa
Yale UP pbk £11.50
0300065434
This is a fresh and illuminating
account of South Africa's eventful history, from the earliest
known human habitation of
the region to the present day.
Thompson, one of the leading
scholars of South Africa, has
produced an elegantly written
narrative that, unlike some
African history, focuses attention
primarily on the experiences of
the black inhabitants rather
than the white minority.

North American History

Ambrose, Stephen
Rise to Globalism
Penguin pbk £8.99
0140175369

Ambrose was personal secretary to Eisenhower during his presidency and his insider's knowledge of the workings of the corridors of power is used to good effect in his study of American policy in the years from 1938 to the present day. The Cold War, Korea, the Cuba invasion and America's progressive entanglement in Vietnam are all subjects on which Ambrose has an illuminating perspective and he also considers Camp David, the Carter administration, war in central America and the invasion of Grenada in this excellent account of America's involvement with the rest of the world over forty years.

Brogan, Hugh
Penguin History of the United States
Penguin pbk £9.99
0140134603

Taking over fifteen years to produce, Hugh Brogan's one-volume history of America is undoubtedly a labour of love. Not a page is wasted as Brogan describes and analyses this immense country from the colonisation of the early British to the humiliation of Nixon's resignation and the withdrawal from Vietnam. Meticulous research and an abundance of detail make the book an essential tool for the student of American History; while the author's obvious passion and admiration for his subject infuse the work with a vibrancy that captures the chaotic energy of a nation as it emerged as the dominating political and cultural influence this century.

Brown, Dee
Bury My Heart at Wounded Knee
Vintage pbk £8.99
0099526409

'We tried to run, but they shot us like we were a buffalo,' said an Indian fleeing from the massacre at Wounded Knee Creek in 1890, where indiscriminate U.S. Calvary cannon and gunfire left hundreds of men, women and children from Big Foot's Minneconjou tribe dead or dying in the frozen landscape. It is Dee Brown's extensive use of such oral recorded history - through interviews, records of treaty councils and other formal meetings - which imbues this book with the pain and anger of a people who saw their long established culture and civilisation obliterated in a little over thirty years. Chronicling that critical period in Indian history from 1860 to 1890, the author has reclaimed the American West from the insidious mythology of 'cowboys', 'mountain men' and 'honourable soldiers'. He tells the stories, wherever possible in their own words, of such famous warriors and chieftains as Sitting Bull, Cochise, Crazy Horse and Geronimo. The grainy black and white photographs that accompany the text add an eerie poignancy to this tragic tale of the American Indian.

Reproduced from *The Oxford Illustrated History of Tudor and Stuart Britain* (Oxford).

Brown, Dee
Wondrous Times on the Frontier
Arrow pbk £6.99
0099153416

Brown is one of America's foremost chroniclers of its Western past and this is a book that draws on more than fifty years of research to provide a memorable portrait of the men and women who endured the hardships and joys, the dangers and the distractions of life on the American frontier. As in Brown's other works of non-fiction, his knowledge of his material is matched by his eye for the telling detail and the revealing anecdote which bring to life the individuals who peopled the frontier.

Carroll & Noble
The Free and the Unfree
Penguin pbk £7.99
0140165401

This challenging interpretation of American history hinges on the relationships between those in power, the possessors of wealth and influence, and those excluded from the opportunities that the nation represented. The United States was a nation created to embody certain principles enshrined in the constitution but frequently when these principles were tested by native Americans, by blacks, by waves of immigrants and by women, they were found wanting.

Countryman, Edward
The American Revolution
Penguin pbk £7.99
014014661X

In the 1770s and 1780s attempts by the British to reassert power over rebellious American colonies escalated into a major war in which those colonies were lost and a new nation created. Countryman's book is a highly readable account of those years which summarises and synthesises recent academic debates on the central characters and key events of the rebellion that developed into a revolution. By introducing the reader to six 'types', from slave to landowner, he recreates vividly the struggle for independence at the level of ordinary experience.

Demos, John
The Unredeemed Captive
Macmillan pbk £10.00
0333650107

In one of the most interesting and stimulating books of American history recently published, Demos tells the resonant story of Eunice Williams, who, as a young girl, was captured by Indians in 1704. For decades her family, including her father and brother, who had themselves been captives for varying periods of time, attempted to 'redeem' her from her captors but Eunice became absorbed in her new culture, forgetting her native language and marrying a Mohawk. Intermittent contact was maintained with her original family until Eunice was an elderly woman but she never returned. She remained 'unredeemed'. As an examination of the disputed territory where two very different cultures meet and interact, as an example of the importance of the 'frontier' in American history, of delineating boundaries between 'civilised' and 'uncivilised' and as a human story of individuals in exceptional circumstances, The Unredeemed Captive works equally well.

Debo, Angie
A History of the Indians of the United States
Pimlico pbk £12.50
071265979X

This book, by a writer who has also been a notable biographer of the Apache guerrilla fighter Geronimo, has been acclaimed by many as the best one-volume survey of the native peoples of the USA. From the Blackfeet to the Sioux, from the Arapahos to the Shoshonis, Debo chronicles the stories of the many different tribes from the time of their first contact with Europeans to the present day. In many ways a depressing story of exploitation and betrayal, it is also a remarkable record of cultural identities surviving, battered but intact, through centuries of encroachment by aggressive and expansionist Europeans.

Donald, David Herbert
Lincoln
Pimlico pbk £12.50
071267330X

Abraham Lincoln rose from the backwoods of Kentucky and Indiana, where he was born and grew up, to become the President who put an end to slavery, won the Civil War and saved the Union from splitting into two. His assassination by John Wilkes Booth ensured his status as an iconic figure in American history. David Herbert Donald, twice winner of the Pulitzer Prize for biography, has looked behind the myth of Lincoln to present a moving portrait of the man as statesman and commander, as husband and father. Convincingly demonstrating the relationship between Lincoln's private life and his public life, Donald's well written and impeccably researched book is likely to remain the best biography of America's sixteenth and, arguably, greatest President for a long time to come.

Foote, Shelby
The Civil War :
Fort Sumter to Perryville
Pimlico pbk £15.00
0712698027

The Civil War :
Fredericksburg to Meridian
Pimlico pbk £15.00
0712698078

The Civil War :
Red River to Appomattox
Pimlico pbk £15.00
0712698124

The war between the Northern states and the Southern states, growing out of the deep divisions between them, particularly over the 'peculiar institution' of slavery, was, in some ways, the first major war of the modern era and prefigured the terrible slaughter of the First World War. More than six hundred thousand Americans lost their lives in the struggle, as the South sought to establish itself as a separate nation, and the effects of the conflict are still apparent in the United States even today. Shelby Foote's epic three volumes which trace the course of the war from the firing of the first shots at Fort Sumter to Lee's signing of the surrender at Appomattox are essential reading for anyone who wants a detailed but gripping narrative of the conflict. Foote has also written fiction and his skills as a storyteller are apparent in his accounts of the engagements, both minor and major, of the war. He also brings vividly to life the personalities of the leading participants in the war. He draws

upon contemporary sources, his own researches and the published works of fellow Civil War historians such as Bruce Catton and Allan Nevins to produce a work that combines painstaking scholarship with immense readability.

Jones, Maldwyn
The Limits of Liberty
Oxford UP pbk £14.99
0198205724

One of the volumes in the Short Oxford History of the Modern World, this is a major survey of the American past from the time of the earliest colonial settlements to the 1992 election.

Josephy, Alvin
500 Nations
Pimlico pbk £20.00
0712674217

As Josephy makes clear in this monumental history of the indigenous peoples of the Americas, the traditional image of the Plains Indian, engaged in a doomed battle with white settlers, represents only the final chapter in a long and sorry saga of suffering and exploitation, which began when Columbus disembarked at Hispaniola to be greeted by its Arawak inhabitants. However Josephy is rightly concerned to emphasise the triumphs as well as the

The American Civil War

A small selection of the hundreds of books available on the American Civil War.

For the general reader interested in the events of the American Civil War the books by Macpherson (see page 150) and by Ward (see page 151) provide, in different ways, excellent one-volume introductions. The three volumes by Shelby Foote (see page 147) form an epic but readable narrative. Another distinguished historian of the war, Bruce Catton, also wrote a one-volume account that has just appeared in a new edition, revised by James MacPherson. **The New History of the Civil War** (Viking 0670868043 £25.00) recreates movingly the events of the war and draws heavily on the words of the men and women who actually experienced the conflict.

Beyond the single-volume history of the war, there is a huge wealth of material, much of it, of course, published in the USA, and enthusiastic amateur historians of the struggle between Union and Confederacy, of whom there are many, have a vast library of publications on which to draw. Brian Reid's **The Origins of the American Civil War** (Longman 0582491789 £16.99) is a recent addition to the scholarly debates about how and why the war began. **The Real War Will Never Get in the Books** (Oxford UP 0195098374 £9.99) presents an interesting perspective on the course of the war through the writings of some of the most sensitive and percipient contemporary observers of it.

Some of the chief campaigns of the Civil War are covered in detailed and finely written books issued by American University Presses. **Decision in the West** (University Press of Kansas 070060748X £15.95) by Albert Castle deals with one of the most important campaigns of the entire war - Sherman's advance on Atlanta, the fierce battles that raged around the city and his victorious 'March to the Sea'. The same University Press also publish a series of guides to Civil War battles including **The Guide to the Battle of Chickamauga** (0700605959 £10.50), which shows how a skirmish developed into one of the bloodiest struggles of the war and one of the Confederacy's finest victories. Da Capo publish a series of Campaigns of the Civil War, many of them reprints of classic accounts such as **Chancellorsville and Gettysburg** (0306805499 £10.50) by baseball-inventing General Abner Doubleday, who was in command of the First Corps at the latter battle.

From Manassas to Appomattox (Konecky & Konecky 0914427695 £14.95) by another veteran general James Longstreet is one of a series of hardback books reissued by the same publishers which are remarkable value for money. Other titles include **The Civil War Reader** (0914427733 £14.95) and **Campaigning with Grant** (0914427709 £14.95) by General Horace Porter. The Civil War, as well as being, arguably, the first war of the modern age, could also be described as the last war in which the military flair and style of individual commanders made a significant difference. **Commanders of the Civil War** (Salamander 086101510X £24.95) is a large format illustrated survey of the leading lights of both Union and Confederate forces. Konecky & Konecky have placed Civil War enthusiasts even more in their debt by reprinting **The Personal Memoirs of Ulysses S. Grant** (09144276279 £14.95) and have published standard works on other gifted generals of the war. **The Invincible Sheridan** (0914427970 £14.95) by Richard O'Connor is a substantial study of the man who, famously, went marching through Georgia and **Jeb Stuart** (0914427741 £14.95) by John Thomason is an account of the flamboyant Confederate general, whose death in the 1864 Wilderness campaign lost the South one of their greatest and most charismatic figures. **Stonewall Jackson and the American Civil War** (Konecky & Konecky 0914427776 £14.95) by G.F.R.Henderson is a study of the life and campaigns of the other great lost hope of the South, the austere and religious Jackson, accidentally shot by his own troops after the battle of Chancellorsville. **General Lee** (DaCapo 0306805898 £12.95) is a reissue of a classic biography of Robert E.Lee by his nephew Fitzhugh Lee, who was a cavalry officer under his uncle's command. **Custer Victorious** (University of Nebraska Press 0803295561 £11.95) is a study of the Civil War career of a man who was the polar opposite of the noble Lee - the charismatic but egotistically demented Custer who was to lead men to die at the Little Big Horn eleven years after the end of the war.

The Civil War provided the stage on which maverick characters like Custer could display their panache. **That Devil Forrest** by John Allan Wyeth (Lousiana State University Press 0807115789 £16.95) is an account of the life of another such character, although one of more substantial talents than Custer. Indeed Sherman described Nathan Bedford Forrest as 'the most remarkable man our Civil War produced on either side.' Operating as a semi-guerrilla fighter on the Confederate side, he was a soldier of near-genius who ended the war still undefeated. **Gray Ghosts of the Confederacy** (Louisiana State University Press 0807111627 £8.95) is a riveting study of those who were unashamedly guerrillas, those like Quantrill, 'Bloody Bill' Anderson and the James brothers who harried the Union forces in brutal skirmishes in the Western states. Finally the similarly-titled **Ghosts of the Confederacy** (Oxford UP 0195054202 £11.95) covers a very different subject. This is a social history of the aftermath of the Civil War, assessing how white American southerners adjusted to and interpreted their defeat in what was the bloodiest war of the nineteenth century.

the ongoing confrontation between English and French language and culture, which has been a major theme and the source of much of the constitutional complexity in Canada's history, to the later part of the twentieth century.

tragedies of native American cultures. The great figures of the Indian nations' history - the Ottawa chieftain and military genius Pontiac, the orator and visionary Tecumseh - are rescued from the condescension of ethnocentric historians. The richness and sophistication of pre-Columban civilisations are given due attention. Perhaps the book's greatest strength is the superb quality of its illustrations. Every page has pictures to pore over, many of them of the glowing artefacts of cultures which have suffered much yet which have, somehow, survived to face the future.

McNaught, Kenneth
Penguin History of Canada
Penguin pbk £8.99
0140149988

First published in 1969 and revised several times in the years since then, McNaught's book is the most readily available and accessible one-volume history of his country. With conciseness and lucidity, he traces the story of Canada from the earliest expeditions, which arrived in search of fish and fur, through

McPherson, James
Battle Cry of Freedom
Penguin pbk £11.00
0140125183

McPherson's greatest achievement, in this one volume history of the American Civil War, is to explain satisfactorily the war's origins. The USA in the first half of the nineteenth century had two very different social and economic systems and an open frontier to the west. Which system should the newly emerging states in the west adopt? Up to the late 1850s it was the South, dominant in the Senate, who won each crucial conflict, yet the new states, for economic reasons, found slavery an unsuitable system. Their citizens tended to be small farmers, not able to afford slaves. Each new state created threatened the South's dominance. McPherson also gives a detailed yet accessible account of the war years themselves, guiding the reader through the politics, economics and military actions of 1860-1865, culminating in Lincoln's discovery of a general, Ulysses S. Grant, willing and able to bring the North's superior manpower and economic strength to bear on the South. Events move inexorably towards the surrender of Lee at Appomattox.

Milner et al
The Oxford History of the American West
Oxford UP pbk £16.99
0195112121

Richly illustrated and based upon the finest scholarship, this book does full justice to the complexities of a subject that is often trivialised or misrepresented. The work of twenty eight leading scholars is brought together to form a volume which examines all aspects of the history, culture and society of the West. The effects of a large increase in population, the destruction of the buffalo herds and their replacement with cattle, the social forces behind the high levels of violence, the disastrous impact of large scale white settlement on the native Americans; these are just some of the topics covered in a volume which should be read by anyone who wants to understand the West.

Tindall, George
America : A Narrative History
Norton pbk £8.95
0393962954

To encompass the entire span of American history in one volume is an ambitious, some might say impossible, task. Tindall and Shi offer a brisk and readable chronological narrative which is accompanied by an array of maps, photographs and illustrations. Their blend of political, social and economic history is deftly achieved and they pay particular attention to the impact that immigration, voluntary and involuntary, has had on America and its consequently multicultural society.

Ward, Geoffrey C.
The Civil War
Pimlico pbk £20.00
0712652345

This book accompanied the award-winning American TV series and is a straghtforward narrative of the conflict, beginning with an examination of its causes and then working progressively through the years 1861 to 1865. The text is illustrated with hundreds of contemporary photographs. The Civil War was one of the first conflicts to be caught by the photographer's lens and the grainy, black and white images reproduced in Ward's book add moving resonance to his text.

Ward, Geoffrey C.
The West : An Illustrated History
Weidenfeld Hbk £30.00
0297821814

Although based on the script of a TV series, this is a substantial book in its own right and a fine re-telling of the epic story of America's self-defining expansion westwards. Ward focuses on the experiences of the innumerable people - from explorers to Indian warriors, from outlaws to homesteaders - who participated in the drama. The book draws upon a wide range of letters, diaries and memoirs and is richly illustrated with hundreds of evocative and moving photographs.

Wright, Ronald
Stolen Continents
Pimlico pbk £12.50
0712657339

In this powerful and moving account of the impact of Europeans on the Americas, Wright gives us history, not as it has been written by the victors in the centuries-long struggle, but the story seen from the viewpoint of the conquered, a story of plague and invasion, of peoples and civilisations destroyed. Taking five peoples – Aztec, Maya, Inca, Cherokee and Iroquois – Wright follows their histories through five centuries, through periods in which these peoples were devastated by the impact of the Europeans and periods in which they struggled to maintain some kind of cultural identity. His book is a valuable reassessment of a story too long seen from one

perspective only. As Eduardo Galeano has said, 'Do you want to know how American Indians 'discovered' Europe? Read this book.'

Zinn, Howard
A People's History of the USA
Longman pbk £18.99
058229472X

Written with the intention of providing a general survey of the history of the United States seen from a radical and non-establishment perspective, Zinn's powerful and combative book is a re-interpretation of the American story which, while acknowledging the achievements of the last two hundred years, is also prepared to examine the costs. It provides a voice for the often voiceless in its reassessment of the American dream and has provoked much debate amongst historians and its many readers since first publication.

Reproduced from *The Oxford Illustrated Encyclopedia of World History Volume 2* (Oxford).

Central and Southern America

Clendinnen, Inga
Aztecs
Cambridge UP pbk £7.95
0521485851

In 1521 an extraordinary sight met the eyes of Hernan Cortes and the small group of conquistadors who had accompanied him into the heart of what is now Mexico. The lakeside city of Tenochtitlan was the magnificent and populous centre of the Aztec empire and the arrival of the Spanish and their Indian allies, ironically, signalled the downfall of a city upon which its eventual conquerors must, on that first day, have gazed with awe. Drawing on the available evidence, Clendinnen reconstructs vividly the culture of the Aztecs in the last decades before the arrival of the Spanish and examines the rites and rituals of the imperial city, including the ceremonies of human sacrifice which so appalled the Spanish.

Coe, Michael D.
Breaking the Maya Code
Penguin pbk £7.99
014023481

The Maya civilisation flourished in Central America from the 3rd to the 10th centuries A.D. but it is only within the last twenty years that the Mayan Glyphs, the pictorial language which has been discovered in the ruins of Copan and other Mayan cities, have been deciphered by scholars. Coe's book gives a first-hand account of the process by which some 85% of the glyphs have now been 'read' and the information they contain revealed. As well as providing new insights into an ancient civilisation, his work also tells a fascinating human story of scholarly rivalries and personality clashes.

Diaz, Bernal
Conquest of New Spain
Penguin pbk £7.99
0140441239

Diaz was one of the small band of Spaniards who accompanied Cortes on the extraordinary expedition which resulted in the subjugation of Montezuma and his Aztec empire. As an old man, fifty years after the events, Diaz wrote this account of what the expedition had seen, suffered and inflicted.

Hemming, John
Red Gold
Papermac pbk £12.00
0333631102

Amazon Frontier
Papermac pbk £12.00
0333617452

Red Gold tells the tragic story of the conquest of the Brazilian Indians in the two and a half centuries from the first landing of the Portuguese in 1500 to the expulsion of the Jesuits from the country in the 1760s. *Amazon Frontier* continues the story through the nineteenth century, with its ongoing encounters and conflicts between newly discovered tribes and the European settlers, and into the early twentieth century, concluding in 1910 with the creation of the Indian Protection Service. John Hemming, veteran of many expeditions to Brazil and someone who knows and has visited many of the remaining tribal peoples of the region, is the ideal person to guide the reader through the sorry tale of how colonial greed and religious fervour decimated Brazil's Indians and to record how, as numbers dramatically declined, the Indians changed status from that of feared enemy to the object of anthropological study.

Williamson, Edwin
Penguin History of Latin America
Penguin pbk £9.99
0140125590

This is probably the best single-volume history of Latin America, designed to guide the general reader from the process of conquest and colonialisation which brought huge tracts of new territory into the control of Spain and Portugal, through to the present day. The book is divided into three parts. The first examines the process of discovery and conquest and the colonial societies that emerged from it. The second narrates the progress of the independence movements of the nineteenth century and the various attempts to produce stable and effective nations and governments that followed independence. The final part analyses the history of Latin America - and particularly the very different stories of Brazil, Mexico, Cuba, Argentina and Chile - in the twentieth century.

Thomas, Hugh
The Conquest of Mexico
Pimlico pbk £14.00
0712660798

In this book Hugh Thomas demonstrates an enviable ability to organise and shape complex material and sources into a very readable account of what occurred when the great Mexican empire of Montezuma collapsed under the onslaught of Cortes and the handful of Spanish conquistadors under his command. The story embodies perhaps the most extraordinary clash of cultures in history, resulting, predictably but with tragic violence, in triumph for one and destruction for the other. Thomas creates a vivid sense of both destroyers and destroyed - the martial fervour and self-conviction of the Spaniards, the life of the Mexicans in their lakeside capital Tenochtitlan - and goes a long way towards answering what seems the most puzzling question about the entire European invasion. How did so few men succeed in conquering such a large and powerful empire in the space of a few years?

Reproduced from the *Illustrated History of Europe (Weidenfeld & Nicolson)*.

Chinese History

Cotterell, Arthur
China : A Concise Cultural History
Pimlico pbk £10.00
0712662510
This exceptionally comprehensive cultural history ranges from the far past to the present - from the turmoil and disunity of pre-Imperial China to the renaissance of the Tang and Sung dynasties, from the Mongol conquest to the events in Tiananmen Square. The book serves simultaneously as an excellent and concise guide to the great stretches of China's past and, through its emphasis on the many continuities there are within the oldest of all civilizations, as an aid to understanding the present China, which has emerged once again, in the years since Mao's revolution, as a significant world power.

Fairbank, John King
China: A New History
Harvard UP pbk £9.95
0674116712
China has claims to be one of the oldest civilisations in the world, with one dynasty of rulers succeeding another from the eighteenth century B.C. to 1911. Fairbank is one of the great historians of China in the west and this, the product of a lifetime of study, is his overview of those centuries which brings the story up to the events in Tiananmen Square in 1989. As Jonathan Spence, another distinguished western historian of the country has written, 'This book is without parallel as a concise, comprehensive and authoritative account of China and its people over four millennia.'

Gernet, Jacques
A History of Chinese Civilisation
Cambridge UP pbk £19.95
0521497817
This revised and updated edition of a work which gained much acclaim when it was first published in 1982 is a broad survey of several thousand years of China's history and culture. From the first formation of a centralised state through such important eras in the country's history as the Han period, the Mandarin empire, the Mongol invasion and occupation, the Ming Dynasty and its achievements and failures, the Manchu rule right up to the revolution and the People's Republic, Gernet provides a reliable guide for both students and the general reader.

Hopkirk, Peter
Foreign Devils on the Silk Road
Oxford UP pbk £6.99
0192814877
Told with all Hopkirk's characteristic verve and vividness, this is the story of the expeditions mounted by a number of archaeological adventurers from the West in search of the treasures of the lost cities of the Silk Road, the medieval route by which trade goods passed from Europe to China and back. The pages of the book are peopled by powerful characters like the Swedish explorer and geographer Sven Hedin and the Budapest-born British archaeologist Sir Aurel Stein, who was still climbing the hills of Central Asia when nearly eighty, and Hopkirk draws on their first-hand accounts to bring to life the perils and rewards that accompanied their exploits.

Salisbury, Harrison
The New Emperors : Mao and Deng
Harper Collins pbk £9.99
0586218645
The death of Deng removed the last link with the generation of Chinese Communists, led by Mao, which brought the People's Republic into existence. In telling the lives of Mao and Deng in this dual biography, Harrison Salisbury is effectively telling also the history of China in the twentieth century. From Mao's first conversion to Marxism in a China only recently ruled by the Manchu dynasty, through the Long March and the civil war with the forces of Chiang-Kai-Shek, the Revolution in 1949, the Cultural Revolution (in which Deng was purged as a 'revisionist'), the return of Deng to power in 1977, the story of these two men is the story of China. Salisbury's book draws on new and previously misinterpreted evidence to produce a fascinating portrait of two extraordinary individuals and the state they have shaped.

Spence, Jonathan
God's Chinese Son
Flamingo pbk £7.99
0006384412May 97
The Taiping rebellion in mid-nineteenth century China is one of the most extraordinary episodes in the history of that country and, although a little-known story in the West, it was a rebellion which cost the lives of twenty million people, either in battle or through starvation. The leader of the rebellion was Hong Xiuquan, who believed himself to be the son of the Christian God. He gathered about him an army of fanatical followers which, through a series of battles, massacres and sieges, took control of a vast swathe of territory in Northern China. Hong ruled over this 'Heavenly Kingdom' for eleven years, slowly descending further into delusion and tyranny. Jonathan Spence, who has written many acclaimed works on China, has used his erudition as a scholar and his skill as a writer to fashion a compelling narrative from this bizarre sequence of events.

Spence, Jonathan
The Search for Modern China
Norton pbk £16.95
0393307808
This is an epic narrative of four centuries of Chinese history, from the waning days of the Ming dynasty to the events in Tiananmen Square, which highlights the efforts of the vast country to achieve a society both Chinese and modern. Spence recounts the achievements and failures of the nation's leaders from the great Qing emperors to the giants of the twentieth century – Sun-Yat-Sen, Chiang Kai-Shek and Mao – and, through his accounts of the periods of rebellion and revolution (1644, 1850, 1911, 1949), the reader can glimpse the ordinary Chinese people struggling to remake their lives.

Asian History

Central Asian History

Ascherson, Neal
The Black Sea
Vintage pbk £7.99
0099593718

The Soviet Empire has disappeared into history. From its ruins new nations, variously defined, are struggling to emerge, some of them on the shores of the Black Sea. Ascherson's book is at once a personal account of some of the events in the old Soviet Union, a wide-ranging history of many of the peoples who have lived around the Black Sea, and a meditation on the ways in which imagined communities of nations are created. Moving from prehistory to the present, Ascherson describes the recurrent encounters between settlers and nomads which form the history of the Black Sea, encounters in which the difficult notions of 'civilization' and 'barbarism' were framed and re-framed.

Inalcik, Halil

The Ottoman Empire 1300-1600
Phoenix pbk £12.99
1857991206

Described by the TLS on its first publication as 'a masterly book',

Inalcik's book covers the classical period of Ottoman history, the period from 1300 to 1600. The empire began as a small military principality but, during these centuries, expanded to become the most powerful of Islamic states, incorporating the old Arab lands, and reaching its fullest extent under the rule of Suleiman the Magnificent. Inalcik not only examines the higher political structure and administration that developed as the empire grew but investigates how everyday life was affected by the expansion. As narrative history and as social history his book is a vivid and readable work.

Indian and South Asian History

Hibbert, Christopher
The Great Mutiny
Penguin pbk £8.99
0140047522

The most serious uprising against British rule in India, rooted in widespread resentments amongst all classes of Indians, was triggered initially by the belief among Indian troops in British service that new cartridges had been greased with animal fat, something

abhorrent to both Muslims and Hindus. The outbreak at Meerut in May 1857 quickly spread to Delhi, which was seized by three mutinous regiments, and British garrisons at Lucknow and Cawnpore were besieged. It was only after much bloodshed that the British regained control and it was July 1858 before peace could be officially declared. Hibbert's renowned skills as a popular historian are evident in this enthralling account of a conflict characterised by the heroism and savagery on both sides.

Hopkirk, Peter
The Great Game
Oxford UP pbk £8.99
0192827995

In 1842, in the Central Asian town of Bokhara, two ragged figures knelt in the dust in the square before the Emir's palace, awaiting execution. They were British officers - Colonel Charles Stoddart and Captain Arthur Conolly - and they were about to pay the price of engaging in the Great Game. The Great Game, a phrase made famous by Kipling in *Kim,* was the shadowy struggle between the rival powers of imperial Britain and Tsarist Russia which took place, for the best part of a century, in the passes and deserts of Central

Asia. As Britain consolidated its rule in India and Russia expanded eastwards and southwards, collision was inevitable and Hopkirk's immensely readable book tells the story of the Great Game through the dramatic exploits of the officers from both sides who risked, and sometimes lost, their lives playing it.

Hopkirk, Peter
On Secret Service East of Constantinople
Oxford UP pbk £6.99
0192853031

In 1914, as the First World War began, an extraordinary plan was hatched by the Germans and their Turkish allies to foment revolutionary uprisings against the British in India and against the Russians in Central Asia. In this grippingly readable sequel to The Great Game, Hopkirk tells the story of the shadowy contests fought between the agents of King and Kaiser, of Tsar and Sultan and recounts some of the adventures and misadventures of the men involved in them.

Hopkirk, Peter
Trespassers on the Roof of the World

Told in Hopkirk's gripping style, this is the story of the opening up of Tibet to Europeans in the nineteenth and early twentieth centuries and the race, involving travellers from a number of nations, to reach the sacred capital of Lhasa. Hopkirk brings to life the extraordinary characters, from secret agents and soldiers to mystics and mountaineers, from the Russian Nikolai Prejevalsky to Sir Francis Younghusband, who participated in the race.

Thapar, Romila
History of India Volume 1
Penguin pbk £7.99
0140138358

Spear, T.G.P.
History of India Volume 2
Penguin pbk £7.99
0140138366

These two well-established books are intended not for the specialist but for those who have a general interest in India and a wish to read a broad survey of its history. The first volume traces the evolution of India over 2,500 years from the establishment of Aryan culture in about 1000 B.C. to the coming of the Mughals in A.D. 1526 and the arrival of the first European trading companies. The second volume adopts the unusual approach of treating the Mughal and British periods in one book, intending, as Spear notes, to highlight large continuities between the two periods. Mughal rule was a preparation and precondition of the modern age ushered in by British rule, and the form that age took was shaped by India's own particular history in the Mughal centuries. Similarly it was the British Raj and the Indian response to it that precipitated the transformation of India that is still in progress.

Reproduced from *The Cambridge Encyclopedia of India* (Cambridge).

Japanese History

Storry, Richard
History of Modern Japan
Penguin pbk £7.99
014013512X
No knowledge of world history is complete without an understanding of the role played by the Japanese. Storry's book is a compact, lucidly written account of their development into one of the most powerful nations on earth. His title is slightly misleading since the book offers a broad sweep of Japanese history, rather than just of the last hundred years. Storry underlines how traditional much of modern Japan is, as well as exploring one of the keys to understanding its culture – the uneasy relationship with the West.

Middle Eastern History

Hourani, Albert
History of the Arab Peoples
Faber pbk £10.99
0571166636
Hourani, a greatly respected Arab scholar, maps out the history of countries where Arabic is the main language and Islam the most widespread religion - beginning in the seventh century and bringing the story to the present day. He uses political changes to provide a chronological framework but relates these to all the forces of society and culture, forging connections between Arab culture and world history.

Watson, Francis
India : A Concise History
Thames & Hudson pbk £7.95
050027164X
Too often attempts to compress Indian history have given overdue prominence to less than two centuries of British ascendancy and eighty nine years of direct rule. Watson, while mindful of the richly eventful period of British rule and its importance in shaping the nation-state of today, sees it as but one episode in a long story of many states and empires that begins in the third millennium B.C. with the Indus Valley civilization. Watson covers such subjects as the empire of the great ruler Ashoka and his heirs in the third century B.C., the impact of Buddhism and Islam and the Moghul conquest in this succinct and well-illustrated book.

Lewis, Bernard
The Middle East
Phoenix pbk £9.99
1857994116
This major work charts two thousand years of history in the Middle East, birthplace of three major world religions, and records its successive transformations from the time of the two great empires, Roman and Persian, to the present day. Lewis is one of the leading Western scholars of the Arabic and Muslim worlds and his writing is alive to the historical processes involved in the development of Christianity, the rise and spread of Islam in the seventh century and the changing balance of power between the Muslim and Christian powers that have characterised many of the most significant events in Middle Eastern history.

Mansfield, Peter
A History of the Middle East
Penguin pbk £8.99
0140125388

This broad survey looks at the Middle East over the last two hundred years, from Napoleon's assault on Egypt, through the long and often painful decline of the Ottoman Empire, to the emergence of today's nations, the Palestinian question and the rebirth of Islamic fundamentalism. Mansfield has reported on the Middle East for many decades and his detailed knowledge is clear in this excellent political overview of the region and its troubled past.

Marshall, Robert
Storm from the East
Penguin pbk £6.99
0140238832

In the 13th century Genghis Khan, a Mongolian warrior leader of military genius, united the tribes of Central Asia, moulded them into a formidable fighting force and carved out an empire which, at the time of his death in 1227, stretched from Korea to the Black Sea. Kublai Khan, his grandson, consolidated the Mongol hold on much of this territory and became the first Mongol emperor of China, although he twice failed to invade and conquer Japan. His court was described by the famous traveller from the West, Marco Polo. Marshall's book, based on a well-received TV series, is a colourful and vivid account of this epic story of Mongol conquest and empire.

Palmer, Alan
The Decline and Fall of the Ottoman Empire
John Murray pbk £14.99
0719552818

Throughout most of the nineteenth century the Ottoman Empire, once so powerful as to threaten Western Europe, was in a state of decline and much diplomatic energy was expended by the great powers, either in hastening or preventing this process. In the aftermath of the First World War the empire was dealt its final death blow by the modernising general, and later president of Turkey, Mustafa Kemal Ataturk. In this rewarding narrative Palmer, although giving due attention to the last years of the empire, sets its collapse in a longer perspective by taking the story back to 1683, when the failure to take Vienna marked the end of Ottoman expansionism towards the West.

Wheatcroft, Andrew
The Ottomans
Penguin pbk £8.99
0140168796

The Ottomans conquered Constantinople in 1453 and, at its peak, their empire included large parts of the Middle East and vast tracts of south-eastern Europe. During its long decline it became known as 'the sick man of Europe' and it finally disintegrated in the aftermath of the First World War. In the West, the Ottomans were an enigma and conflicting myths developed - the Ottomans as barbarous and bloodthirsty savages contrasted with the Ottomans as over-civilised and effete sybarites. Wheatcroft's book is not a narrative history of the empire - although it draws much of its material from that history - but a penetrating investigation of the realities behind the myths.

Australasian History

Clark, Manning
History of Australia
Pimlico pbk £15.00
0712662057

Manning Clark is one of Australia's foremost historians. His six volume History of Australia, published between 1956 and 1986, is a unique contribution to his country's historiography. This one volume abridgement by Michael Cathcart retains the distinctive tone of voice in Manning Clark's writing but brings his vast vision of Australia's development from 1788 to the mid-twentieth century to the attention of the general reader daunted by the multi-volume work.

Hughes, Robert
The Fatal Shore
Harvill pbk £7.99
1860461506

Written with a combination of real narrative verve and indisputably thorough research, Hughes' epic book traces the history of the 'convict years' of Australia's human history; from the arrival of 160,000 men women and children in Botany Bay in May 1787 to the despatch of the very last convict ship to Western Australia in 1868. Principally known as an art critic and broadcaster, Hughes struck upon the need for a history of convict Australia through the acknowledgement of how little he, born and educated in Australia, actually knew about the colonial past of his own country, and from his conviction that there were attempts to ignore a section of history unpalatable to contemporary Australians. The resulting text, almost immediately a best-seller on publication, is a vivid re-enactment of that history. This can make for gory reading - this was an age of brutal punishment and fear, of almost inconceivable hardship and atrocity - but this is popular history at its very best. The attention to detail, the wit in Hughes' passionate prose and his accomplished style mark the book out as a definitive work.

Military History

Beevor, Antony
Crete : The Battle and the Resistance
Penguin pbk £7.99
0140167870

Beevor recounts the fall of Greece, the battle of Crete and the Resistance from beginning to end, overturning previous interpretations of the battle by demonstrating the central significance of a misinterpreted Ultra Intelligence signal in dictating the outcome of the conflict. Beevor's narrative is at once a clear account of the military operations and an extremely readable portrait of the many flamboyant characters, including Patrick Leigh Fermor and Evelyn Waugh, who participated in the irregular warfare on the island.

Bunting, Madeleine
The Model Occupation
HarperCollins pbk £7.99
0006379737

The Channel Islands surrendered to invading German forces in July 1940. For nearly five years, until May 1945, they remained under occupation and recent opening of archives has revealed the extent of the Channel Islanders' collaboration with, as well as resistance to, the German troops stationed there. This book is a fascinating account of those five years of occupation, the everyday life of the islanders during that period and the everyday moral dilemmas that many of them had to face.

Chandler, David
The Campaigns of Napoleon
Weidenfeld Hbk £40.00
0297748300

Chandler is acknowledged as, perhaps, the leading expert on Napoleonic warfare and this monumental, 1100 page survey of Napoleon's entire military career, from the siege of Toulon to his ultimate defeat at Waterloo, is his magnum opus. Every campaign and battle that Napoleon fought is described in great detail and maps, of a high standard, accompany many of them. Numerous appendices and a wide-ranging bibliography complete a book that no enthusiast for the period should be without.

Clark, Alan
Barbarossa: The Russian-German Conflict
Phoenix pbk £10.99
1857992504

On June 22nd 1941 the German Army rolled across the Russian frontier and thus began Barbarossa, the German invasion of the Soviet Union. The clash between two totalitarian systems, two dictators and two of the greatest armies in history lasted four years and moved from Leningrad to Moscow, from Stalingrad to Kursk and then rolled back towards Berlin and the ultimate German humiliation. Using much material unavailable to earlier historians, Alan Clark has fashioned an account of one of the most gruelling and bloody campaigns of any war, in which the reader is shown both the strategy of Hitler, Stalin and their generals, and the ordeals of the soldiers in the front line.

Clark, Alan
The Donkeys
Pimlico pbk £10.00
0712650350

Originally published in 1961, *The Donkeys* remains one of the most popular works on the First World War. The title comes from the famous reply of the German general Hoffmann to his colleague's comment that the British soldiers fought like lions 'True. But don't we know that they are lions led by donkeys.' The book concentrates on the events of 1915, culminating in the Battle of Loos, which saw a British casualty rate of 80%, and recounts the deadly frailties and shortcomings of the generalship and the heroism of the ordinary soldiers.

Clausewitz, Karl von
On War
Penguin pbk £7.99
0140444270

Published after his death in 1831, Clausewitz's *On War* is one of the most influential books ever written about military strategy. Most famous for its dictum that war is a continuation of political policy by other means, the book has been required reading for students of military theory ever since. The philosophy of 'Total War' - war between whole nations, not just armies on a battlefield - has coloured much modern strategic thinking and also bears much responsibility for the exceptionally bloody nature of much modern war.

Contamine, Philip
War in the Middle Ages
Blackwell pbk £15.99
0631144692

Covering a thousand year period, from the fifth century to the fifteenth, this book is a mine of information on its subject. From the barbarian invasions of the Roman Empire, through the Norman conquest of Britain and the Crusades, to the Hundred Years' War, every aspect of medieval warfare is examined. Containing details on developments in arms, armour, fortifications and tactics, whilst placing them in their social contexts, this is a work that History Today has called, 'Quite simply, the best book on medieval European warfare available in any language'.

Dear, Ian & Foot, M.R.D. (eds)
Oxford Companion to the Second World War
Oxford UP hbk £30.00
0192141686

A recent addition to the Oxford Companion series, this is the best work of reference on World War Two available to the general reader. An international collaboration by more than 140 experts, it contains over 1,750 entries and 120 maps. Entries range from the narrowly focused to the wide-ranging, with technical information on weaponry, details of battles and tactics as well as essays covering social and political issues. In many cases, entries include suggestions for further reading, making it an indispensable work for both researchers and military buffs.

Reproduced from *The Oxford Illustrated History of Tudor and Stuart Britain (Oxford)*.

Deighton, Len
Blitzkrieg
Pimlico pbk £10.00
0712674284

Blood, Tears and Folly
Pimlico pbk £8.99
071266226X

Fighter
Pimlico pbk £10.00
0712674233

In his three books on the
Second World War, Deighton
brings the narrative skills of a
novelist to bear on the events,
particularly those of the first
three years of the war, in
volumes which have thoroughly
engaged both general readers
and professional historians.
In *Fighter* he probes behind the
myths of the Battle of Britain
to reveal, without denigrating
the heroism of those who flew
the planes, how much the
struggle was one between
technologies and machines.
Blitzkrieg illuminates the German
tactics of fast-moving surprise
attacks by tanks and armoured
vehicles, backed by close air
support, which won them such
swift victories against Poland and
France, and narrates their swift
dash to the Channel coast in
1940 and the debacle that was
Dunkirk. *Blood, Tears and Folly*,
subtitled *An Objective Look at
World War II,* is an ambitious
endeavour to tell the story of
what happened in the crucial
years from the invasion of
Czechoslovakia to Pearl Harbour
and its aftermath, and to locate
that within a larger historical
perspective.

Dixon, Norman
**On the Psychology of Military
Incompetence**
Pimlico pbk £10.00
0712658890

From the disastrous Crimean
campaign to the heroic but
doomed battle for Arnhem,
this fascinating book examines
failures in recent British military
history. Traditionally such
failures have been blamed on
individual errors of judgement,
even stupidity. Norman Dixon,
however, argues that only by
understanding the wider culture
of the military can we explain
them. By drawing on theories
of personality, group behaviour
and decision-making, he builds a
psychological model of modern
armies and their commanders
and suggests that this model
can inevitably lead to disaster.

Ellis, John
The Sharp End
Pimlico pbk £12.50
0712658912

In their own words ordinary
allied soldiers describe what it
was like to be at 'the sharp end'
in World War Two. Not only is
the experience of combat vividly
described but the book also
covers topics as diverse as
patrols, disease, being wounded,
morale, food and combat
fatigue. Indeed the book is a
convincing study of the entire
experience of being at war,
one that records movingly the
comradeship that kept men and
units together in the face of the
most appalling dangers.

Ellis, John
**The Social History of the
Machine Gun**
Pimlico pbk £9.00
0712656693

Although prototypes exist from
the eighteenth century, the
machine gun was essentially a
product of the second half of
the nineteenth century. Gatling
invented his gun in the US
during the American Civil War
and Hiram Maxim devised his
gun, the first to be genuinely
automatic rather than hand-
cranked, in the eighteen
eighties. John Ellis's study of
the machine gun makes clear
how it revolutionised warfare,
in the Civil War, in the various
colonial wars of the periods and,
above all, in the First World
War in which it dominated the
battlefields from the outset.

Fussell, Paul
The Great War and Modern Memory
Oxford UP pbk £8.99
0195021711

In this book Fussell illuminates the British experience of fighting on the Western Front and examines the way that experience has been fundamental to the culture, throughout the years since 1918, by focusing on the literary means by which the War has been remembered and mythologized. Drawing on the poems of writers like David Jones and Wilfred Owen and on the memoirs of Sassoon, Robert Graves and Edmund Blunden, as well as the personal records of lesser known individuals, Fussell has produced a work of cultural history that offers a truly different perspective on its subject.

Gilbert, Martin
The First World War
HarperCollins pbk £10.99
0006376665

Martin Gilbert is one of the foremost historians of the Twentieth Century and has written the definitive one-volume history of the Great War. Drawing on many sources, the narrative weaves together the political, strategic and social strands of the conflict from a variety of viewpoints. Much use is made of contemporary letters, diaries and memoirs to provide a fascinatingly intimate picture of the feelings and experiences of participants from all sides.

Gilbert, Martin
The Second World War
Phoenix pbk £14.99
1857993462

Martin Gilbert is one of the few writers with the scholarship and breadth of vision required for the mammoth task of weaving the many aspects of the Second World War into a coherent narrative. His principal concern in this book is to show what happened and to attempt to present events not from a narrow perspective but from a global one. He is triumphantly successful and the result is a work that deserves the highest praise - a sweeping, thousand page history that encompasses both the grand strategies of the war and the experiences of the individual soldiers.

Hastings, Max
The Korean War
Macmillan pbk £10.00
0333591534

The Korean War was the first major war of the nuclear age. Communist North Korea invaded the South in June 1950 and the United Nations responded by sending forces, mainly American but including British troops, under the command of Douglas MacArthur, to defend the rapidly overrun South. Mao's new communist regime in China supported the North and the war soon became a stalemate, although peace was not signed until July 1953. Max Hastings, the well-known journalist and military historian, has written a compelling narrative of the war which is much the best single volume account aimed at the general reader.

Hastings, Max
On the Offensive
Pan pbk £9.99
0330346075
Bringing together in one volume all three of Max Hastings' books on the Second World War, *On the Offensive* is popular military history of the highest order and excellent value for money. *Bomber Command* is the story of the RAF's bombing campaign against Germany and of the sacrifices of the many aircrew who died. *Overlord* charts the D-Day landings and the two months of fighting which followed. *Das Reich* recounts the actions of the elite 2nd Panzer Division in its attempts to reach the Normandy landings, and the Allied efforts to stop it.

Hibbert, Christopher (ed)
Recollections of Rifleman Harris
Windrush Press pbk£9.99
0900075634
'All I can do is to tell the things which happened immediately around me, and that, I think, is as much as a private soldier can be expected to do.' This modest quote conveys the essence of Benjamin Harris's memoir of life in the 95th Rifles. Narrated in simple language, it covers the period of Wellington's Peninsular War against Napoleon. It portrays vividly the privations suffered by the common soldier on campaign.

Holmes, Richard
Fatal Avenue
Pimlico pbk £10.00
0712658351
'The Fatal Avenue' was De Gaulle's description of the swathe of territory north and east of Paris, the land bounded on the west by the Channel and on the east by the valley of the Moselle, in which so much of the most bitter warfare in European history has taken place. Richard Holmes' book, subtitled *A Traveller's History*, looks at all the major battles which have taken place in the fatal avenue and relates their tactics and strategies to the terrain on which they were fought. From Agincourt and Crécy to Verdun and Ypres, from Joan of Arc and Marlborough to Haig and Foch, Holmes provides an original and thought-provoking guide to the battles of Northern France and Flanders and those who fought them.

Holmes, Richard
Firing Line
Pimlico pbk £10.00
0712661573
Holmes's ambitious book draws upon written accounts of war from the last two centuries, and from the oral testimony of those who have fought in the major conflicts of this century, to produce a study which focuses on fundamental questions about the nature of human behaviour in battle. What does motivate men to risk appalling injury and loss of life in time of war? How do they maintain the will to go on fighting in conditions of the utmost physical and mental degradation? In facing up to these questions, Holmes throws light on many aspects of soldiering and warfare - the importance of charismatic leadership, the sustaining power of comradeship - in a work that combines scholarship with humanity and psychological insight.

Holmes, Richard
Riding the Retreat
Pimlico pbk £10.00
0712658629

In a book that is a stimulating and original blend of military history and travel literature, Richard Holmes follows in the footsteps of the British Expeditionary Force in its retreat in 1914 from Mons to the banks of the Marne, where the German advance was stopped. Holmes and four companions ride along the route of the retreat, passing through the battlefields of the campaign and the cemeteries which house many of those who fought on those battlefields, and he weaves together the two parallel stories of his own journey and the events of 1914 into a compelling narrative.

Horne, Alistair
The Price of Glory
Penguin pbk £8.99
0140170413

Verdun was a battle which lasted nearly a year, a battle in which almost three quarters of a million casualties fell along a fifteen mile front, a battle in which the attritional nature of trench warfare reached a bloody culmination. Alistair Horne's book is a comprehensive account of one of the most significant engagements of World War I and a moving study of the men who fought and died in it.

Kagan, Donald
On the Origins of War
Pimlico pbk £14.00
0712673504

Kagan's volumes on the Peloponnesian War have received extraordinary acclaim and this investigation of the origins of war analyses in detail the situation and events that led to the outbreak of that war as well as three other conflicts - the First World War, the Second Punic War and the Second World War - and the superpower standoff which might have resulted in the most catastrophic war of all, the Cuban Missile Crisis. His work adds both to the historical understanding of the wars he considers and to a much-needed understanding of how conflict escalates.

Reproduced from *The Oxford Illustrated History of Modern Europe (Oxford)*.

Keegan, John
Battle at Sea
Pimlico pbk £10.00
0712659919

Battle at Sea is a study of the use of naval power and the way it has changed over time. Four great battles are described with the same eye for detail that characterised *The Face of Battle* and are put in their strategic contexts. Keegan describes Trafalgar, which ended the threat of invasion from Napoleon; Jutland, which ended the German naval threat in the First World War; Midway, which marked a turning point in America's war with Japan and the Battle of the Atlantic, which kept the lifeline to Britain open in the Second World War.

Karnow, Stanley
Vietnam
Pimlico pbk £15.00
071265965X

Often described as the definitive history of the conflict, Karnow's monumental narrative clarifies and analyses the tragedy of the Vietnam War and puts the events and decisions of the day into sharp, clear focus. Karnow, an eminent journalist and foreign correspondent and the winner of a Pulitzer Prize for an earlier historical work on American involvement in the Philippines, has drawn widely on published and unpublished sources and upon hundreds of interviews with the diplomats and journalists, the military commanders and government officials, the soldiers and medics who participated in the war, to construct his massive history.

Keegan, John
The Face of Battle
Pimlico pbk £10.00
0712650903

John Keegan is greatly respected by both academic and general readers and this is one of his most popular works. The book looks at three of the most famous battles in history – the carnage of Agincourt, the smoke and confusion of Waterloo and the bloody stalemate of the Somme. This is a soldier's eye view of war, vividly conveying the physical pressures and experience of battle. We are reminded that, despite obvious differences in scale and technology, the human response to extreme danger has remained the same throughout history.

Keegan, John
The Mask of Command
Penguin pbk £8.99
0140114068

Telling the stories of four famous leaders and their very different styles of leadership, this book is an examination of the changing nature of military command. Keegan describes Alexander the Great, the Heroic Leader, who led from the front and risked as much as his men; Wellington, the Anti-Heroic Leader, who led on the battlefield but remained aloof; Ulysses S. Grant, the Unheroic Leader, who respected his troops for risking all, while he remained in the rear, and Adolf Hitler, the False-Heroic Leader, who manufactured an aura of heroism but went nowhere near the battlefield.

Keegan, John
A History of Warfare
Pimlico pbk £8.99
0712698507

A work of staggering breadth, this is John Keegan's master-piece. The evolution of military technology is charted, from its primitive origins, through use of metals, the introduction of the horse, the gunpowder revolution, up to the nuclear age. As his central themes expand, Keegan includes many absorbing diversions into specific areas of history and includes essays on topics such as logistics and fortifications. He marries all this to a profound understanding of the cultural influences on warfare, making his work as much a history of civilisation as of war.

Keegan, John
Warpaths
Pimlico pbk £9.99
0712673261

This is an engaging combination of military history and travel book in which Keegan describes his long love affair with America, and tours its landscapes in search of the significant campaigns and battles that have been fought on American soil. He demonstrates how geography can explain military history, how, in America particularly, climate and competition for natural resources explain why men fortified where they did, campaigned where they did and were drawn to the battlefields where major issues were decided. Yorktown, the cam-paigns of the Civil War and the Battle of the Little Big Horn are some of the subjects covered in this original and enjoyable book.

Keegan, John (ed)
Who's Who in World War II
Routledge pbk £10.99
0415118891

Three hundred of the most important figures in the war from the British Field Marshal Auchinleck to the Russian Marshal Zhukov are described in concise but authoritative biographies. The majority of the entries cover military leaders but there are also entries on politicians and propagandists, diplomats and demagogues, from Charles De Gaulle to Tokyo Rose.

Keegan, John & Wheatcroft, Andrew (eds)
Who's Who in Military History
Routledge pbk £10.99
0415118840

This reference work, broad in its geographical and chronologi-cal scope, offers detailed biographies of those figures who have shaped the course of war from 1453 to the present day. The book also includes a series of maps to illustrate the main theatres of war in the period.

Reproduced from *The Oxford Illustrated History of Modern Europe (Oxford)*.

Liddell-Hart, Basil
History of the First World War
Macmillan pbk £10.00
0333582616

History of the Second World War
Macmillan pbk £12.99
0333582624

Liddell-Hart (1895-1970) had only a brief, active military career himself – he was an infantry officer in World War I – but he was a much respected and influential military historian and theorist for much of his life, an early advocate of the importance of airpower and armoured forces. Although Liddell-Hart's reputation suffered its ups and downs and he was out of favour with the military establishment for much of the Second World War, his histories of the two world wars remain valuable and readable works.

Liddell-Hart, Basil (ed)
Letters of Private Wheeler
Windrush Press pbk £9.99
0900075589

This is one of the best examples of an ordinary soldier's perspective on warfare. Private Wheeler of the 51st provides us with a vivid portrait of everyday life in a regiment as well as of frontline experience of many battles in the Napoleonic Wars. Edward Blishen described Wheeler as 'a natural storyteller.....someone whose gift was to bring everything he wrote about to life' and his letters, enhanced by background notes, are skilfully edited by Liddell-Hart. From Corunna to Waterloo, Wheeler was present and his honest and perceptive comments make a valuable and entertaining addition to our understanding of the realities of soldiering.

Macdonald, Lyn
The Somme
Penguin pbk £7.99
0140178678

Lyn Macdonald's books on the First World War have been widely praised. They are most notable for the space she devotes to the voices of those who took part. Based on hundreds of interviews, *Somme* tells the story of the battle from the initial build-up to the horror of the assault, as experienced by the British troops who were there. The battle, which resulted in nearly a million casualties, has come to symbolise the brutality and waste of the war and this book is a worthy testament to the men who fought.

Kruger, Rayne
Goodbye, Dolly Gray
Pimlico pbk £12.50
0712662855

In the Boer War the British Empire, at the height of its powers, faced its greatest military challenge since the Crimean War. In colonial wars only the Zulus had inflicted anything like a significant defeat on imperial armies. The Boers, descendants of Dutch colonists to the Cape, who had formed their own independent republics in South Africa, defeated the British three times in one week, the so-called 'Black Week', and laid siege to Mafeking and two other important townships. Only the massive influx of reinforcements sent to South Africa enabled the British to regain the upper hand. Taking his title from a song of the period, Rayne Kruger brilliantly describes the background, the arms and armies, the campaigns and personalities of the war.

MacDonald, Lyn
1914

Penguin pbk £7.99
0140116516

Another of MacDonald's meticulously detailed books drawn from the testimony of World War One survivors, this conveys movingly the growing sense of disillusionment which the first months of the war brought. Her first chapter 'All in a Day's Work' shows motivated and hopeful troops arriving in France at the start of the war but, as the book progresses, the developing fatigue and fatalism of the soldiers are made clear and, as the winter of 1914 sets in, the eye-witness accounts reflect the harrowing conditions in which they found themselves. Once again Macdonald's willingness to allow a voice to the participants themselves has produced an affecting and impressive book.

MacDonald, Lyn
The Roses of No Man's Land

Penguin pbk £8.99
014017866X

Macdonald is a skilled oral historian and, in this book, she gathers together the moving and first-hand accounts of volunteer nurses and doctors who served on the Western Front during World War One. From them she has fashioned a story of courage and endurance, of ordinary people thrown into terrible and extraordinary circumstances, trying to cope with unprecedented carnage and devastation. MacDonald's commitment to the use of survivors' testimony makes her account of the mental and physical suffering of the wounded, and of the desperation of medical staff forced to try new and daring techniques in order to alleviate that suffering, all the more compelling.

Macdonald, Lyn
1915: The Death of Innocence

Penguin pbk £9.99
0140259007

Her earlier books established Lyn Macdonald as one of the leading chroniclers of the First World War and a writer superbly adept at incorporating first-hand material letters, diaries and interviews with survivors into a compelling narrative. In this book she turns her technique on the events of 1915, a year that, as Macdonald herself notes, has been strangely neglected. The first months of the year, despite the appalling setbacks of 1914, were a time of hope in which men and officers alike looked forward to campaigns that would break the deadlock and force the Germans to retreat. By the end of the year, the bloody battlefields of Neuve Chapelle, Ypres and Loos and the disaster at Gallipoli had swept away all the old ideas of warfare, although many were slow to acknowledge it. In this sense 1915 represented, as Macdonald's subtitle states, the death of innocence.

Macdonald, Lyn
They Called It Passchendaele

Penguin pbk £7.99
0140165096

The Third Battle of Ypres resulted in a bitter and appalling bloodbath for a ridge and small village named Passchendaele. Over a million British, Canadian and Anzac troops took part. This book recounts memories of the mud, terror, comradeship and disillusionment from the perspective of the survivors of the conflict. Using the same methods and procedures that characterise her previous books, Lyn Macdonald presents the reader with a haunting and remarkable appreciation of one of the costliest campaigns in history.

Massie, Robert K.
Dreadnought
Pimlico pbk £15.00
0712653686

Dreadnought is a huge and gripping chronicle of the British and German naval rivalry which began in the 1890s and culminated in the great 'Dreadnought' battles of the First World War. Massie, who won the Pulitzer Prize for his biography of Peter the Great, is renowned for his sense of the dramatic and for his capacity to recreate historical figures as rounded and vigorous personalities on the page, and this epic book is filled with vivid portraits of the central characters in the quest for naval supremacy, from Balfour and Bismarck to Admiral von Tirpitz and the young Winston Churchill. The rivalry between the two major protagonists, Britain and Germany, was embodied by Edward VII and his nephew Kaiser Wilhelm, and the strange and increasingly difficult relationship between them is at the heart of this vast and illuminating narrative.

Middlebrook, Martin
Arnhem 1944
Penguin pbk £9.99
0140143424

Operation Market Garden could have shortened the war. A daring airborne attack into Nazi-held Holland to seize vital road bridges was intended as a springboard for a thrust into Germany itself. The attack was dogged by bad luck and met much stronger opposition than anticipated, none more so than at Arnhem, where British paratroops, attempting to hold the bridge, made one of the most heroic stands of the war. Over 500 interviews with participants and extensive use of original documents have gone into this detailed account of the battle for the 'bridge too far'.

Middlebrook, Martin
The First Day on the Somme
Penguin pbk £8.99
0140171347

The terrible slaughter of British troops on the first day of this battle is vividly and movingly portrayed in this book. In just one day the Army suffered 60,000 casualties and achieved nothing. By interviewing many of the ageing survivors of the battle, before their memories and oral testimony were lost forever, the author succeeded in producing a chilling account of the heroism, the scale of suffering and losses, the sheer pointless stupidity of war in general and this battle in particular. As one private memorably summed up the day, 'It was pure bloody murder.....the cream of British manhood was shattered in less than six hours.'

Overy, Richard
Why the Allies Won
Pimlico pbk £12.50
0712674535

Was the Allied victory in the Second World War inevitable? Could the outcome have been different? Richard Overy's masterly strategic survey addresses these central questions. Challenging some cherished assumptions, the book makes clear that simple theories do not explain the way events unfolded. Some Allied victories were narrow ones; hindsight gives a false impression of supremacy over the Axis powers. It was a complex mixture of factors which led to ultimate victory, economic and techno-logical developments combined with less tangible political and social factors. It was these strengths, not enemy weaknesses, that were decisive.

Padfield, Peter

The War Beneath the Sea

Pimlico pbk £14.00
0712673814

Padfield has written lives of many of the leading figures of the Third Reich, including Hess and Himmler. In this book, he turns his attention from individuals to the conflict between U-boat and submarine that was such an important part of the war between the Allies and the Nazi regime, and to the submarine campaigns of the other combatant nations. His absorbing account provides a salutary reminder of the narrowness of the margin of victory in the sequence of operations known as the Battle of the Atlantic, and of just how close the Axis forces came to achieving their aim of stopping supplies from North America reaching Britain.

Pakenham, Thomas

The Boer War

Abacus pbk £10.99
0349104662

Of all the wars in which Britain engaged between 1815 and 1914, the Boer War was the longest, the costliest, the bloodiest and, because of the defeats inflicted by the Boer republics and their ability to tie down British forces in long sieges at towns like Mafeking and Ladysmith, the most humiliating. Pakenham's readable and prize-winning account, based on a vast array of first-hand and often unpublished sources, came out in 1979 and is still the best one-volume history of the war for the general reader.

Read, Anthony

The Fall of Berlin

Pimlico pbk £12.50
0712657975

As Allied armies converged on the city and Hitler's regime descended further into its madness and paranoia, the battle for Berlin raged, one of the most violent struggles ever for the possession of a city. Read and Fisher's book provides a coherent and comprehensible account of the battle, of the war viewed from the perspective of the Red Army approaching from the river Oder, and of the strategy of the RAF in its earlier efforts to bomb the Nazi government into submission. Incidentally the book gives a more general picture of the city in the war years and of the life of its citizens.

Rodger, N. A. M.

The Wooden World

Fontana pbk £9.99
0006861520

Partly through popular fiction and film, images of the eighteenth century navy are plentiful. Tyrannical officers wield the lash to keep at bay a near-mutinous crew; filth, disease and rotting rations abound on board ship while drunkenness and the press gang are ubiquitous ashore. If this were an entirely true picture, however, how would one explain the paradox that the Royal Navy was the most efficient and effective force of the age, growing in size during the century and attaining a near-total supremacy on the seas. Widely researched, this book paints the true picture of naval life and shows that, whilst far from perfect, it merely reflected Georgian society as a whole.

Schom, Alan
Trafalgar
Penguin pbk £9.99
0140111646

Trafalgar was more than just a battle. It was, in Alan Schom's words, 'the culmination of an intense twenty-nine month campaign waged by the Royal Navy to prevent a French invasion of Britain.' Schom's book, an ideal account for the general reader, looks at events in the two years leading up to the battle, from 1803 when Napoleon gave orders for an army and flotilla to invade England, through Pitt and the navy's response to that threat, to the battle itself and Nelson's triumph.

Weigley, Russell
The Age of Battles
Pimlico pbk £14.00
0712658564

The book is subtitled *The Quest for Decisive Warfare from Breitenfeld to Waterloo.* The Swedish victory at Breitenfeld in 1631 proved a watershed in military development in Europe. Old doctrines, unchanged since Roman times, were discarded to be replaced by a new drill and discipline, forming the basis of modern professional armies. Russell Weigley's book is a detailed study of the evolution of military tactics and technology and the birth of strategy during a tumultuous period in European history.

Winter, Denis
Death's Men
Penguin pbk £7.99
0140168222

Death's Men examines the First World War through the eyes of the individual soldier. Using oral and written reminiscences, Denis Winter paints an accurate picture of the life of the ordinary soldier in and out of the trenches. Every aspect of army life is dissected – training, trench life, the strain of battle, attitudes to the Germans and the difficulties of adjusting to civvy street after the War. In this highly readable and accessible book, Denis Winter takes the war from the generals and politicians and returns it to the men who fought in it and, through their words, renews its reality for his readers.

Winter, Denis
Haig's Command
Penguin pbk £9.99
014007144X

Douglas Haig is one of the most controversial soldiers in British history. Appointed in 1915 to succeed French as commander-in-chief on the Western Front, he was largely responsible for the planning and conduct of those battles - the Somme, Arras - which were so costly in human terms and which have haunted the British imagination since. He was also able to lay claim to military success in the Battle of Amiens and the last hundred days in which the Germans were driven to sue for peace. Winter examines in detail Haig's record as commander-in-chief and endeavours to expose what he sees as a major historical fraud, involving the alteration and rewriting of documents of the period, in the construction of Haig's reputation.

Woodham-Smith, Cecil
The Reason Why
Penguin pbk £7.99
0140012788

There are very few events in British military history to equal the tragic farce that was the Charge of the Light Brigade. In *The Reason Why* Cecil Woodham-Smith analyses the entire episode and explains how the mismanagement and obstinate pride of the two commanders, Lords Lucan and Cardigan, proved so fatal. Woodham-Smith's attention to detail and her flair for narrative create a moving account of the six hundred's ride into the Valley of Death.

Illustrated History Paperbacks Series

Sutton Publishing's Illustrated History Paperbacks Series is a wide-ranging and eclectic series of books on subjects as diverse as Women in Ancient Egypt and The English Civil War. All the titles are richly illustrated and lucidly written by acknowledged authorities in the field. At £10.99 each they represent excellent value for money. The full list of titles is:

Arthur: The King in the West
R W Dunning 0750909943

Battle of Bosworth
M Bennett 0862994268

Battle of Towton
A W Boardman 0750912456

Battles of Barnet & Tewkesbury
P W Hammond 0750903740

Conquest
J Peddie 0750915390

Cromwellian Gazetteer
P Gaunt 0750900638

Culloden and the '45
J Black 0750903759

Elizabethan Underworld
G Saldago 0750909765

English Civil War
M Ashley 0750900199

Enterprise of England
R Whiting 0750909935

Food and Feast in Medieval England
P W Hammond 0750909927

Gunpowder Plot
A Haynes 0750912464

Henry VIII and his Queens
D Loades 0750912472

Henry VIII and the Invasion of France
C Cruickshank 0750906782

Hereward
V Head 0750912448

History of Vanity
J Woodforde 0750909773

Invisible Power
A Haynes 0750906766

King Arthur's Place in Prehistory
W A Cummins 0750906642

Knight in Medieval England
P Coss 075090996X

Ladies of the Manor
P Horn 0750914319

Lambert Simnel & the Battle of Stoke
M Bennett 0750903775

Making of the Tudor Dynasty
R Griffiths 0862994276

Man Behind the Iron Mask
J Noone 0750906790

Margaret of York, Duchess of Burgandy
C Weightman 0750903783

Medieval Warhorse
A Hyland 075091243X

Military Campaigns of Wars of the Roses
P Haigh 0750914300

Picts and the Scots
L & J Laing 0750906774

Rise & Fall of the Victorian Servant
P Horn 0750909781

Roman War Machine
J Peddie 0750910232

War for America
J Black 0750906758

Wars of the Roses
J R Lander 0750900180

Women in Ancient Egypt
B Watterson 0750906804

Services at Waterstone's

Recommendation

Our booksellers really know and care about what they are selling. If you need help, please don't hesitate to ask.

Writers at Waterstone's

Ask at your branch for details of author events.

Waterstone's Mailing Service

If you wish to order your books by post, please contact Waterstone's Mailing Service, 4-5 Milsom Street, Bath BA1 1DA

Booksearch

Waterstone's Booksearch service will try to track down out-of-print books for you. Booksearch, 32-40 Calverley Road, Tunbridge Wells, TN1 2TD

Signed First Editions

A choice of up to 150 of the year's finest fiction and non-fiction titles – all signed by the author and posted to you. Waterstone's Signed First Editions Collection, 4-5 Milsom Street, Bath BA1 1DA

Waterstone's Book Vouchers

Accepted in over 500 bookshops in the United Kingdom and Ireland, including all branches of WH Smith.

For information about any Waterstone's service, please ask a bookseller.

Where to find your nearest Waterstone's

ABERDEEN
236 Union Street
Tel: 01224 571655

BATH
4–5 Milsom Street
Tel: 01225 448515

University of Bath
Claverton Down
Tel: 01225 465565

BELFAST
Queen's Building
8 Royal Avenue
Tel: 01232 247355

BIRMINGHAM
24–26 High Street
Tel: 0121 633 4353
Fax: 0121 633 4300
Young Waterstone's
Tel: 0121 616 1557

BOURNEMOUTH
14/16 The Arcade
Tel: 01202 299449

BRADFORD
The Wool Exchange
Tel: 01274 723127

University of
Bradford,
Great Horton Road
Tel: 01274 727885

Management
Centre Bookshop,
Emm Lane
Tel: 01274 481404

BRIGHTON
55–56 North Street
Tel: 01273 327867

BRISTOL
27–29 College Green
Tel: 0117 925 0511

Computer Centre
University of Bristol
Tyndall Avenue
Tel: 0117 925 4297

The Galleries
Broadmead
Tel: 0117 925 2274
Fax: 0117 925 9275

BROMLEY
20-22 Market Square
Tel: 0181 464 6562

CAMBRIDGE
6 Bridge Street
Tel: 01223 300123
Fax: 01223 301539

CANTERBURY
20 St Margarets St
Tel: 01227 456343

CARDIFF
2a The Hayes
Tel: 01222 665606

CARMARTHEN
Trinity College
Carmarthen
Tel: 01267 238100

CHELTENHAM
88–90 The
Promenade
Tel: 01242 512722

CHESTER
43–45 Bridge Street
Row
Tel: 01244 328040

COLCHESTER
The Old Library
16 Culver Precinct
Tel: 01206 767623

University of Essex
Wivenhoe Park
Tel: 01206 864773

CORK
69 Patrick Street
Tel: 00 353 21
276522

Boole Library
Basement,
University College
Tel: 00 353 21
276575

CROYDON
1063 Whitgift Centre
Tel: 0181 686 7032

DERBY
78-80 St Peter's
Street
Tel: 01332 296997

DORKING
54–60 South Street
Tel: 01306 886884

DUBLIN
7 Dawson Street
Tel: 00 353 16 791260

Jervis Centre
Dublin 1
Tel: 00353 16 8781311

DUNDEE
35 Commercial
Street,
Tel: 01382 200322

DURHAM
69 Saddler Street
Tel: 0191 383 1488

EASTBOURNE
120 Terminus Road
Tel: 01323 735676

EDINBURGH
128 Princes Street
Tel: 0131 226 2666

13–14 Princes Street
Tel: 0131 556 3034/5

83 George Street
Tel: 0131 225 3436

EPSOM
113 High Street
Tel: 01372 741713

EXETER
48–49 High Street
Tel: 01392 218392

GATESHEAD
17 The Parade
Metro Centre
Tel: 0191 493 2715

GATWICK
North Terminal
Airside
Gatwick Airport
Tel: 01293 507112

GLASGOW
132 Union Street
Tel: 0141 221 0890

45–50 Princes Square
Tel: 0141 221 9650

GUILDFORD
35–39 North Street
Tel: 01483 302919

**HANLEY,
STOKE-ON-TRENT**
The Tontines
Centre
Parliament Row
Tel: 01782 204582

HULL
University of Hull
University House
Tel: 01482 444190

The Grand
Buildings,
Jameson Street
Tel: 01482 580234

IPSWICH
15 -19 Buttermarket
Tel: 01473 289044

**KINGSTON-UPON-
THAMES**
23–25 Thames Street
Tel: 0181 547 1221

LANCASTER
2–8 King Street
Tel: 01524 61477

LEAMINGTON SPA
Unit 1, Priorsgate
Warwick Street
Tel: 01926 883804

LEEDS
36–38 Albion Street
Tel: 0113 242 0839

93–97 Albion Street
Tel: 0113 244 4588

LEICESTER
The Shires
21/23 High Street
Tel: 0116 251 6838

LIVERPOOL
52 Bold Street
Tel: 0151 709 0866

LONDON

CAMDEN
128 Camden High
Street NW1
Tel: 0171 284 4948

*CHARING CROSS
ROAD*
121 Charing Cross
Road WC2
Tel: 0171 434 4291

THE CITY
1 Whittington Ave
Leadenhall Market
EC3
Tel: 0171 220 7882

COVENT GARDEN
9 Garrick Street
WC2
Tel: 0171 836 6757

EARL'S COURT
266 Earl's Court
Road SW5
Tel: 0171 370 1616

GOLDSMITH'S
Goldsmith's College
New Cross SE14
Tel: 0181 469 0262

HAMPSTEAD
68 Hampstead High
Street NW3
Tel: 0171 794 1098

HARRODS
87 Brompton Road
SW1
Tel: 0171 730 1234
Fax: 0171 225 5920

ISLINGTON
10-12 Islington
Green, N1
Tel: 0171 704 2280

KENSINGTON
193 Kensington High
Street W8
Tel: 0171 937 8432

NOTTING HILL
39 Notting Hill Gate
W11
Tel: 0171 229 9444

*OLD BROMPTON
ROAD*
99 Old Brompton
Road SW7
Tel: 0171 581 8522

WIMBLEDON
12 Wimbledon
Bridge SW19
Tel: 0181 543 9899

MAIDSTONE
19 Earl Street
Tel: 01622 681112

MAILING SERVICE
(see Bath Milsom St)
Tel: 01225 448595
Fax: 01225 444732

MANCHESTER
91 Deansgate
Tel: 0161 832 1992

MIDDLESBROUGH
9 Newton Mall
Cleveland Centre
Tel: 01642 242682

Teesside
University Bookshop
1 King Edward
Square
Tel: 01642 242017

NEWCASTLE
104 Grey Street
Tel: 0191 261 6140

NORTHAMPTON
19 Abington Street
Tel: 01604 34854

NORWICH
Royal Arcade
Tel: 01603 632426

University of East
Anglia,
University Plain
Tel: 01603 453625

NOTTINGHAM
1–5 Bridlesmith Gate
Tel: 0115 9484499

PERTH
St John's Centre
Tel: 01738 630013

PETERBOROUGH
6 Queensgate
Tel: 01733 313476

PLYMOUTH
65/69 New George
Street
Tel: 01752 256699

PRESTON
3–5 Fishergate
Tel: 01772 555766

READING
89a Broad Street
Tel: 01734 581270

**RICHMOND-UPON-
THAMES**
2–6 Hill Street
Tel: 0181 332 1600

SALISBURY
7/9 High Street
Tel: 01722 415596

SHEFFIELD
24 Orchard Square
Tel: 0114 2728971

SHREWSBURY
18–19 High Street
Tel: 01743 248112

SOUTHAMPTON
69 Above Bar
Tel: 01703 633130

Southampton
Medical School,
South Academic
Block,
Southampton
General Hospital
Tel: 01703 780602

University of
Southampton,
Highfield
Tel: 01703 558267

SOUTHEND-ON-SEA
49-55 High Street
Tel: 01702 437480

SOUTHPORT
367 Lord Street
Tel: 01704 501088

STOCKPORT
103 Princes Street
Tel: 0161 477 3755

**STRATFORD-UPON-
AVON**
18 The High Street
Tel: 01789 414418

SWANSEA
The Old Carlton
Cinema,
Oxford Street
Tel: 01792 463567

SWINDON
27 Regent Street
Tel: 01793 488838

TAUNTON
County Hotel
East Street
(opening late May)

TUNBRIDGE WELLS
32/40 Calverley Road
Tel: 01892 535446

WATFORD
174-176 The
Harlequin Centre,
High Street
Tel: 01923 218197

WINCHESTER
1/2 Kings Walk
Tel: 01962 866206

WORCESTER
95 High Street
Tel: 01905 723397

YORK
28–29 High Ousegate
Tel: 01904 628740

£1 off

any title in the Sutton Illustrated History Paperback series

Cut out this coupon, fill in your name and address on the reverse
and we shall happily give you £1 off any title in the
Sutton Illustrated History Paperback Series.

This coupon is worth £1 off a single purchase of any title in the Sutton Illustrated Paperback Series.
It is valid until 31st December 1997 and may not be transferred for cash.
The information overleaf is covered and bound by the terms and conditions of the Data Protection Act and will be
used only in connection with products and services provided by Waterstone's.

- -

£1 off

any HarperCollins History title in this guide

Cut out this coupon, fill in your name and address on the reverse
and we shall happily give you £1 off any HarperCollins history title in this book.

This coupon is worth £1 off a single purchase of any HarperCollins History title. It is valid until 31st December 1997 and may not be transferred
for cash. The information overleaf is covered and bound by the terms and conditions of the Data Protection Act and will be used only in
connection with products and services provided by Waterstone's.

- -

£1 off

any Penguin History title in this guide

Cut out this coupon, fill in your name and address on the reverse
and we shall happily give you £1 off any
Penguin History title in this book.

This coupon is worth £1 off a single purchase of any Penguin History title in this guide. It is valid until 31st December 1997 and may
not be transferred for cash. The information overleaf is covered and bound by the terms and conditions of the Data Protection Act and
will be used only in connection with products and services provided by Waterstone's.

Name...

Address...

....

....

....

....Postcode..............................

Please tick this box if you do not wish to receive further information about Waterstone's □

For booksellers users only:

Branch ....Till Receipt no..............................Amount spend.......................

Name...

Address...

....

....

....

....Postcode..............................

Please tick this box if you do not wish to receive further information about Waterstone's □

For booksellers users only:

Branch ....Till Receipt no..............................Amount spend.......................

Name...

Address...

....

....

....

....Postcode..............................

Please tick this box if you do not wish to receive further information about Waterstone's □

For booksellers users only:

Branch ....Till Receipt no..............................Amount spend.......................